Great Science Adventures

The World of Tools and Technology

D1598036

Dinah Zike
and
Susan Simpson

Great Science Adventures is a comprehensive project which is projected to include the titles below. Please check our website, www.greatscienceadventures.com, for updates and product availability.

Great Life Science Studies:
    The World of Plants
    The World of Insects and Arachnids
    Discovering the Human Body and Senses
    The World of Vertebrates

Great Physical Science Studies:
    The World of Tools and Technology
    The World of the Light and Sound
    Discovering Atoms, Molecules, and Matter

Great Earth Science Studies:
    The World of Space
    Discovering Earth's Landforms and Surface Features
    Discovering the Ocean
    Discovering Earth's Atmosphere and Weather

Copyright © 2001 by:
    Common Sense Press
    8786 Highway 21
    P.O. Box 1365
    Melrose, FL 32666
    (352) 475–5757
    www.greatscienceadventures.com

Rev 11/07

Printed in the United States of America
ISBN 10: 1-929683-06-5
ISBN 13: 978-1-929683-06-2

The authors and the publisher have made every reasonable effort to ensure that the experiments and activities in this book are safe when performed according to the book's instructions. We assume no responsibility for any damage sustained or caused while performing the activities or experiments in *Great Science Adventures*. We further recommend that students undertake these activities and experiments under the supervision of a teacher, parent, and / or guardian.

Great Science Adventures

Table of Contents

Great Science Adventures

Introduction

Great Science Adventures is a unique, highly effective program that is easy to use for teachers as well as students. This book contains 24 lessons. The concepts to be taught are clearly listed at the top of each lesson. Activities, questions, clear directions, and pictures are inclined to help facilitate learning. Each lesson will take one to three days to complete.

This program utilizes highly effective methods of learning. Students not only gain knowledge of basic science concepts, but also learn how to apply them.

Specially designed *3D Graphic Organizers* are included for use with the lessons. These organizers review the science concepts while adding to your students' understanding and retention of the subject matter.

This *Great Science Adventures* book is divided into four parts:

1) Following this *Introduction* you will find the *How to Use This Program* section. It contains all the information you need to make the program successful. The *How to Use This Program* section also contains instructions for Dinah Zike's *3D Graphic Organizers*. Please take the time to learn the terms and instructions for these learning manipulatives.

2) In the *Teacher's Section,* the numbered lessons include a list of the science concepts to be taught, simple to complex vocabulary words, and activities that reinforce the science concepts. Each activity includes a list of materials needed, directions, pictures, questions, written assignments, and other helpful information for the teacher.

   The *Teacher's Section* also includes enrichment activities, entitled *Experiences, Investigations, and Research.* Alternative assessment suggestions are found at the end of the *Teacher's Section.*

3) The *Lots of Science Library Books* are next. These books are numbered to correlate with the lessons. Each *Lots of Science Library Books* will cover all the concepts included in its corresponding lesson. You may read the *Lots of Science Library Books* to your students, ask them to read the books on their own, or make the books available as research materials. Covers for the books are found at the beginning of the *Lots of Science Library Books* section. (Common Sense Press grants permission for you to photocopy the *Lots of Science Library Books* pages and covers for your students.)

4) *Graphic Pages,* also listed by lesson numbers, provide pictures and graphics that can be used with the activities. They can be duplicated and used on student–made manipulatives or students may draw their own illustrations. The *Investigative Loop* at the front of this section may be photocopied as well. (Common Sense Press grants permission for you to photocopy the *Graphics Pages* for your students.)

Great Science Adventures

How to Use This Program

This program can be used in a single level classroom, multilevel classroom, homeschool, co-op group, or science club. Everything you need for a complete tool study is included in this book. Intermediate students will need access to basic reference materials.

Take the time to read the entire *How to Use this Program* section and become familiar with the sections of this book described in the *Introduction*.

Begin a lesson by reading the *Teacher Pages* for that lesson. Choose the vocabulary words for each student and the activities to complete. Collect the materials you need for these activities.

Introduce the lesson with the *Lots of Science Library Book* by reading it aloud or asking a student to read it. (The *Lots of Science Library Books* are located after the *Teacher's Section* in this book.)

Discuss the concepts presented in the *Lots of Science Library Book,* focusing on the ones listed in your *Teacher's Section*.

Follow the directions for the activities you have chosen.

How to Use the Multilevel Approach

The lessons in this book include basic content appropriate for grades K–8 at different mastery levels. For example, throughout the teaching process, a first grader will be exposed to a lot of information but should not be expected to retain all of it. In the same lesson, a sixth–grade student will learn all the steps of the process, be able to communicate them in writing, and be able to apply that information to different situations.

In the *Lots of Science Library Books,* the words written in larger type are for all students. The words in smaller type are for upper level students and include more scientific details about the basic content, as well as interesting facts for older learners.

In the activity sections, icons are used to designate the levels of specific writing assignments.

This icon ✎ indicates the Beginning level, which includes the non reading or early readin student. This level applies mainly to kindergarten and first grade students.

This icon ✎✎ is used for the Primary level. It includes the reading student who is still workir to be a fluent reader. This level is designed primarily for second and third graders.

This icon ✎✎✎ denotes the Intermediate level, or fluent reader. This level of activities w usually apply to fourth through eighth grade students.

If you are working with a student in seventh or eighth grade, we recommend using the assignments fe the Intermediate level, plus at least one *Experiences, Investigations, and Research* activity per lesson

No matter what grade level your students are working on, use a level of written work that appropriate for their reading and writing abilities. It is good for students to review data they alread know, learn new data and concepts, and be exposed to advanced information and processes.

Vocabulary Words

Each lesson contains vocabulary words used in the content of the lesson. Some of these words will l "too easy" for your students, some will be "too hard," and others will be "just right." The "too eas" words will be used automatically during independent writing assignments. Words that are "too har can be used during discussion times. Words that are "just right" can be studied by definition, usag and spelling. Encourage your students to use these words in their own writing and speaking.

You can encourage beginning students to use their vocabulary words as you reinforce readi instruction and enhance discussions about the topic, and as words to be copied in cooperative writin or teacher guided writing.

Primary and Intermediate students can make a Vocabulary Book for new words. Instructions fe making a Vocabulary Book are found on page 3. The Vocabulary Book will contain the word definitio and sentences composed by the student for each word. Students should also be expected to use the vocabulary words in discussions and independent writing assignments. A vocabulary word with asterisk (*) next to it is designated for Intermediate students only.

Using 3D Graphic Organizers

The *3D Graphic Organizers* provide a format for students of all levels to conceptualize, analyze, review, and apply the concepts of the lesson. The *3D Graphic Organizers* take complicated information and break it down into visual parts so students can better understand the concepts. Most *3D Graphic Organizers* involve writing about the subject matter. Although the content for the levels will generally be the same, assignments and expectations for the levels will vary.

Beginning students may dictate or copy one or two "clue" words about the topic. These students will use the written clues to verbally communicate the science concept. The teacher should provide various ways for the students to restate the concept. This will reinforce the science concept, and encourage the students in their reading and higher order thinking skills.

Primary students may write or copy one or two "clue" words and a sentence about the topic. The teacher should encourage students to use vocabulary words when writing these sentences. As students read their sentences and discuss the concept, they will reinforce the science concept, increasing their fluency in reading, and higher order thinking skills.

Intermediate students may write several sentences or a paragraph about the topic. These students are also encouraged to use reference materials to expand their knowledge of the subject. As tasks are completed, students enhance their abilities to locate information, read for content, compose sentences and paragraphs, and increase vocabulary. Encourage these students to use the vocabulary words in a context that indicates understanding of the words' meanings.

Illustrations for the *3D Graphic Organizers* are found on the *Graphics Pages* and are labeled by the lesson number and a letter, such as 5–A. Your students may either use these graphics to draw their own pictures, or cut out and glue them directly on their work.

Several of the *3D Graphic Organizers* expand over a series of lessons, For this reason, you will need a storage system for each students' *3D Graphic Organizers*. A pocket folder or a reclosable plastic bag works well. See page 1 for more information on storing materials.

Investigative Loop™

The *Investigative Loop* is used throughout *Great Science Adventures* to ensure that your labs are effective and practical. Labs give students a context for the application of their science lessons, so that they begin to take ownership of the concepts, increasing understanding as well as retention.

The *Investigative Loop* can be used in any lab. The steps are easy to follow, user friendly, and flexible.

Each *Investigative Loop* begins with a **Question or Concept.** If the lab is designed to answer a question, use a question in this phase. For example, the question could be: "How does a wheel and axle magnify force?" Since the activity for this lab will show how a wheel and axle magnifies force, a question is the best way to begin this *Investigative Loop.*

If the lab is designed to demonstrate a concept, use a concept statement in this phase, such as: "Tools make work easier." The lab will demonstrate that fact to the students.

After the **Question or Concept** is formulated, the next phase of the *Investigative Loop* is Research and/or Predictions. Research gives students a foundation for the lab. Having researched the question or concept, students enter the lab with a basis for understanding what they observe. Predictions are best used when the first phase is a question. Predictions can be in the form of a statement, a diagram, or a sequence of events.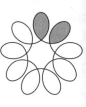

 The **Procedure** for the lab follows. This is an explanation of how to set up the lab and any tasks involved in it. A list of materials for the lab may be included in this section or may precede the entire *Investigative Loop*.

Whether the lab is designed to answer a question or demonstrate a concept, the students' **Observations** are of prime importance. Instruct the students concerning what they are to focus upon in their observations. The Observation phase will continue until the lab ends.

 Once observations are made, students must **Record the Data**. Data may be through diagrams or illustrations. Recording quantitative or qualitative observations of the lab is another important activity in this phase. Records may be kept daily for an extended lab or at the beginning and end for a short lab.

Conclusions and/or Applications are completed when the lab ends. Usually the data records will be reviewed before a conclusion can be drawn about the lab. Encourage the students to defend their conclusions by using the data records. Applications are made by using the conclusions to generalize to other situations or by stating how to use the information in daily life.

 Next we must **Communicate the Conclusions**. This phase is an opportunity for students to be creative. Conclusions can be communicated through a graph, story, report, video, mock radio show, etc. Students may also participate in a group presentation.

Questions that are asked as the activity proceeds are called **Spark Questions.** Questions that the lab sparks in the minds of the students are important to follow and discuss when the lab ends. The lab itself will answer many of these questions, while others may lead to a new *Investigative Loop*. Assign someone to keep a list of all Spark Questions.

 One lab naturally leads to another. This begins a new *Investigative Loop*. The phase called **New Loop** is a brainstorming time for narrowing the lab down to a new question or concept. When the new lab has been decided upon, the *Investigative Loop* begins again with a new Question or Concept.

ke the time to teach your students to make qualitative and quantitative observations. Qualitative servations involve recording the color, texture, shape, smell, size (as small, medium, large), or any rds that describe the qualities of an object. Quantitative observations involve using a standard unit measurement to determine the length, width, weight, mass or volume of an object.

students will make a Lab Book, in the form of a Pocket Book, to store information about the estigative Loops. Instructions for making a Pocket Book are found on page 2. Your students will ke a new Lab Book as needed to glue side–by–side to the previous one. Instructions can be found the *Teacher's Section*.

edictions, data, and conclusions about the *Investigative Loops* are usually written on Lab Record rds. These can be 3– x 5–inch index cards or paper cut to size.

nen you begin an *Investigative Loop*, ask your students to glue or draw the graphic of the experiment the pocket of the Lab Book. Each *Investigative Loop* is labeled with the lesson number and another mber. These numbers are also found on the corresponding graphics. The completed Lab Record rds will be labeled by Lab Number and placed in the appropriate pocket.

ring an *Investigative Loop*, beginning students should be encouraged to discuss their answers to all eriment questions. By discussing the topic, the students will not only learn the science concepts d procedures, but will be able to organize their thinking in a manner that will assist them in later rs of writing. This discussion time is very important for beginning students and should not be hed.

er the discussion, work with the students to construct a sentence about the topic. Let them copy sentence. Students can also write "clue" words to help them remember key points about the eriment and discuss it at a later time.

mary students should be encouraged to verbalize their answers. By discussing the topic, students l learn the science concepts and procedures and learn to organize their thinking, increasing their lity to use higher level thinking skills. After the discussion, students can complete the assignment ing simple phrases or sentences. Encourage students to share the information they have learned :h others, such as parents or friends. This will reinforce the content and skills covered in the lesson.

en though Intermediate students can write the answers to the lab assignments, the discussion ocess is very important and should not be skipped. By discussing the experiments, students review e science concepts and procedures as well as organize their thinking for the writing assignments. is allows them to think and write at higher levels. These students should be encouraged to use their cabulary words in their lab writing assignments.

Design Your Own Experiment

er an *Investigative Loop* is completed, intermediate students have the option to design their own periments based on that lab. The following procedure should be used for those experiments.

Select a Topic based upon an experience in an *Investigative Loop*, science content, an observation, high-interest topic, a controversial topic, or a current event.

Discuss the Topic as a class, in student groups, and with knowledgeable professionals.

Read and Research the Topic using the library, the Internet, and hands-on investigations an observations, when possible.

Select a Question that can be investigated and answered using easily obtained reference material specimens, and/or chemicals, and make sure that the question selected lends itself to scientifi inquiry. Ask specific, focused questions instead of broad unanswerable questions. Questions migh ask "how" something responds, influences, behaves, determines, forms, or is similar or different t something else.

Predict the answer to your question, and be prepared to accept the fact that your prediction might b incorrect or only partially correct. Examine and record all evidence gathered during testing that bot confirms and contradicts your prediction.

Design a Testing Procedure that gathers information that can be used to answer your question. Mak sure your procedure results in empirical, or measurable, evidence. Don't forget to do the following:

> Determine where and how the tests will take place–in a natural (field work) or controlled (lat setting.

> Collect and use tools to gather information and enhance observations.
> Make accurate measurements. Use calculators and computers when appropriate.

> Plan how to document the test procedure and how to communicate and display resulting dat

> Identify variables, or things that might prevent the experiment from being "fair." Befor beginning, determine which variables have no effect, a slight effect, or a major effect on you experiment. Create a method for controlling these variables.

Conduct the Experiment carefully and record your findings.

Analyze the Question Again. Determine if the evidence obtained and the scientific explanations the evidence are reasonable based upon what is known, what you have learned, and what scientis and specialists have reported.

Communicate Findings so that others can duplicate the experiment. Include all pertinent researc measurements, observations, controls, variables, graphs, tables, charts, and diagrams. Discus observations and results with relevant people.

Reanalyze the Problem and if needed, redefine the problem and retest. Or, try to apply what wa learned to similar problems and situations.

Ongoing Project: Timeline Book

e of the activities in Lesson 1 is to make an Accordion Book for the Timeline Book. This will be an going project for your students. In each *Lots of Science Library Book,* the **Tools in Time** pages istrate tools used in a specific location of the world and their date of use. In the Graphics Pages are identical pictures of these tools with a map behind them. Your students will use a copy of se tool graphics to cut out and glue on the appropriate page in the Timeline Book. After the picture glued in place, ask your students to draw a line from the picture to the correct time on the line, and or the location on the map where the tool was used. Encourage students to complete independent search on other tools for the Timeline Book. Following the *Teacher's Section* is a list of additional ls that students can research and add to their Timeline Books.

Ongoing Projects: Problem Solving and Inquiry Scenarios

the Graphic Pages, following the *Investigative Loop,* you will find the Problem Solving and Inquiry enarios. Photocopy this page for your students. Allow the students to work on one or more of these enarios while completing this study of Tools and Technology. Although designed for intermediate dents, all students may participate if possible.

Ongoing Project: Technology Book

ginning in Lesson 4, the *Lots of Science Library Books* include information on the history of chnology. At the end of each *Teacher's Section*, there is a section entitled **Technology** that has more ormation and an assignment for the students. Located at the end of the Graphics Pages are the **chnology Graphics** for these assignments. We suggest that the Technology unit be completed by ler students in addition to the other activities. More information is located in the *Teacher's Section* Lesson 4.

Experiences, Investigations, and Research

the end of each lesson in the *Teacher's Section* is a category of activities entitled *Experiences, estigations, and Research.* These activities expand upon concepts taught in the lesson, provide a ndation for further study of the content, or integrate the study with other disciplines. The following ns are used to identify of the type of each activity.

Tools

Hands On

Writing

History

Literature

Math

Research

Cumulative Project

At the end of the program we recommend that students compile a Cumulative Project using th activities they have completed during their course of study. It may include the Investigative Loops, La Record Cards, and the *3D Graphic Organizers* on display.

Please do not overlook the Cumulative Project, as it provides immeasurable benefits for your student Students will review all the content as they create the project. Each student will organize the materi in his or her own unique way, providing an opportunity for authentic assessment and reinforcing th context in which it was learned. This project creates a format where students can make sense of th whole study in a way that cannot be accomplished otherwise.

ast Food and Fast Folds

"making the manipulatives takes up too much of your instructional time, they are not worth doing. ey have to be made quickly, and they can be, if the students know exactly what is expected of them. mburgers, Hot Dogs, Tacos, Mountains, Valleys, and Shutter–Folds can be produced by students, who turn use these folds to make organizers and manipulatives."– Dinah Zike

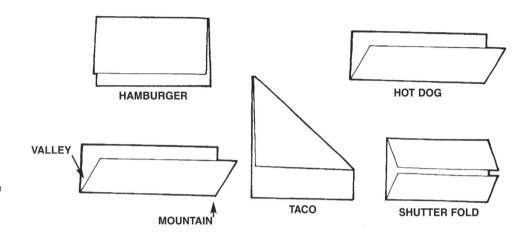

ery fold has two parts. The tside edge formed by a fold is led the **"Mountain."** The inside this edge is the **"Valley."**

torage – Book Bags

ne–gallon reclosable plastic bags are ideal for storing ongoing projects and books at students are writing and researching.

e strips of clear, 2" tape to secure 1" x 1" pieces of index card to the front and ck of one of the top corners of a bag, under the closure. Punch a hole through e index cards. Use a giant notebook ring to keep several of the "Book Bags" gether.

bel the bags by writing on them with a permanent marker.

ternatively, the bags can be stored in a notebook if you place the 2" clear tape ong the side of the storage bag and punch 3 holes in the tape.

lalf Book

ld a sheet of paper in half like a Hamburger.

HAMBURGER

Large Question and Answer Book

1. Fold a sheet of paper in half like a Hamburger. Fold it in half again like a Hamburger. Make a cut up the Valley of the inside fold, forming two tabs.

2. A larger book can be made by gluing Large Question and Answer Books "side–by–side."

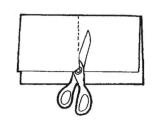

Small Question and Answer Book

1. Fold a sheet of paper in half like a Hot Dog.

2. Fold this long rectangle in half like a Hamburger.

3. Fold both ends back to touch the Mountain top.

4. On the side forming two valleys and one Mountain top, make vertical cuts through one thickness of paper, forming tabs for questions and answers. These four tabs can also be cut in half, making eight tabs.

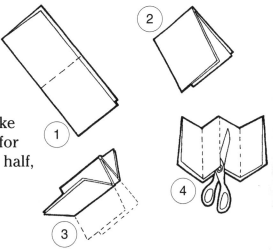

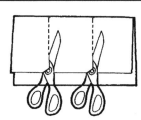

3 Tab Book

1. Fold a sheet of paper in half like a Hamburger or Hot Dog. Fold it into thirds. Cut the inside folds to form three tabs.

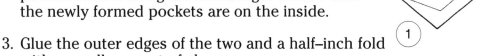

Pocket Book

1. Fold a sheet of paper in half like a Hamburger.

2. Open the folded paper and fold one of the long sides up two and a half–inch inches to form a pocket. Refold along the Hamburger fold so that the newly formed pockets are on the inside.

3. Glue the outer edges of the two and a half–inch fold with a small amount of glue.

4. Make a multi–paged booklet by gluing several Pocket Books "side–by–side."

5. Glue a construction paper cover around the multi–page pocket booklet.

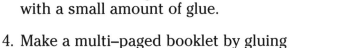

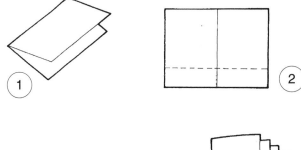

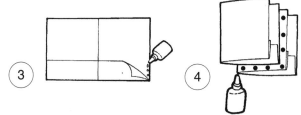

Vocabulary Book

. Take two sheets of paper and fold each sheet like a Hot Dog.

. Fold each Hot Dog in half like a Hamburger. Fold each Hamburger in half two more times and crease well. Unfold the sheets of paper, which are divided into sixteenths.

. On one side only, cut the folds up to the Mountain top, forming eight tabs. Repeat this process on the second sheet of paper.

. Take a sheet of construction paper and fold like a Hot Dog. Glue the back of one vocabulary sheet to one of the inside sections of the construction paper. Glue the second vocabulary sheet to the other side of the construction paper fold.

. Vocabulary Books can be made larger by gluing them "side–by–side."

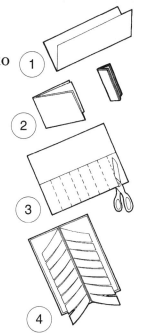

Pyramid Project

Fold a sheet of paper into a Taco.
Cut off the excess tab formed by the fold.

Open the folded taco and refold it the opposite way forming another taco and an X fold pattern.

Cut up one of the folds to the center of the X and stop. This forms two triangular–shaped flaps.

Glue one of the flaps under the other flap, forming a pyramid.

Set the Pyramid up on one end or glue two or more together to make a diorama.

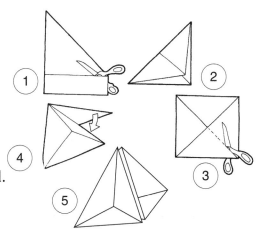

Layered Look Book

Stack two sheets of paper and place the back sheet one inch higher than the front sheet.

Bring the bottom of both sheets upward and align the edges so that all of the layers or tabs are the same distance apart.

When all tabs are an equal distance apart, fold the papers and crease well.

Open the papers and glue them together along the Valley/center fold.

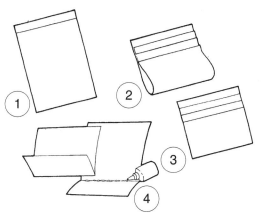

4 Door Book

1. Fold a sheet of paper into a Shutter Fold.

2. Fold it into a Hamburger.

3. Open the Hamburger and cut the Valley folds on the Shutters only, creating four tabs.

   Refold it into a Hamburger, with the fold at the top. Decorate the top sheet as the cover.

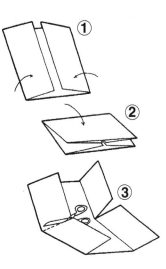

Bound Book

1. Take two sheets of paper and fold each like a Hamburger.

2. Mark both folds 1" from the outer edges.

3. On one of the folded sheets "cut up" from the top and bottom edge to the marked spot on both sides.

4. On the second folded sheet, start at one of the marked spots and "cut out" the fold between the two marks. Do not cut into the fold too deeply, just shave it off.

5. Take the "cut up" sheet and roll it. Place it through the "cut out" sheet and then open it up. Fold the bound pages in half to form a book.

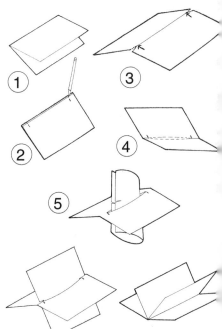

Variation...

To make a larger book, use additional sheets of paper, marking each sheet as explained in #3. Use an equal number of sheets for the "cut up" and "cut out." Place them one on top of the other and follow the directions in #4 and #5.

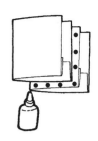

ide–by–Side

Some books can easily grow into larger books by gluing them side–by–side. Make two or more of these books. Be sure the books are closed, then glue the back cover of one book to the front cover of the next book. Continue in this manner, making the book as large as needed. Glue a cover over the whole book.

ccordion Book

Fold each section of paper into a Hamburger; however, fold one side 1/2 inch shorter than the other side. This will form a tab that is 1/2 inch long.
Fold this tab back away from the shorter piece of paper. Do not fold this tab over the short side, fold it the opposite way.

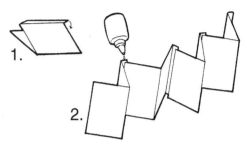

Glue together to form an accordion by gluing a straight edge of one section into the Valley of another section.

ote: Stand the sections on end and form an accordion with them before gluing. (See illustration.)

he *Lots of Science Library Book* Shelf

ake a bookshelf for the *Lots of
cience Library Books* by using a box of
 appropriate size or by following the
structions below.

Begin with an 11" x 12" piece of poster board or cardboard.
Mark lines 3" from the edge of each side. Fold up along each line.
Cut on the dotted lines as indicated in Illustration #1.
Refold on the lines.

Glue the tabs under the top and bottom sections of the shelf. See Illustration 2.
Cover your shelf with attractive paper.

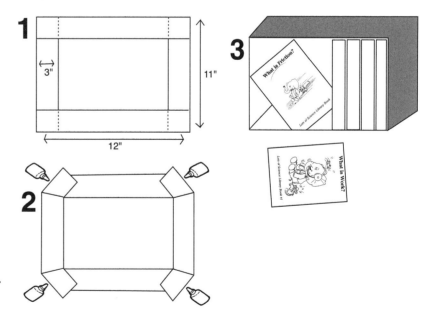

If you are photocopying your *Lots of Science Library Books*, consider using green paper for the covers and the same green paper to cover your bookshelf.

Great Science Adventures

Teacher's Section

Website addresses used as resources in this book are accurate and relevant at the time of publication. Due to the changing nature of the Internet, we encourage teachers to preview the websites prior to assigning them to students.

The authors and the publisher have made every reasonable effort to ensure that the experiments and activities in this book are safe when performed according to the book's instructions. We recommend that students undertake these activities and experiments under the supervision of a teacher, parent, and/or guardian.

Tools Concept Map
Lessons 1–4
Numbers Refer to Lesson Numbers

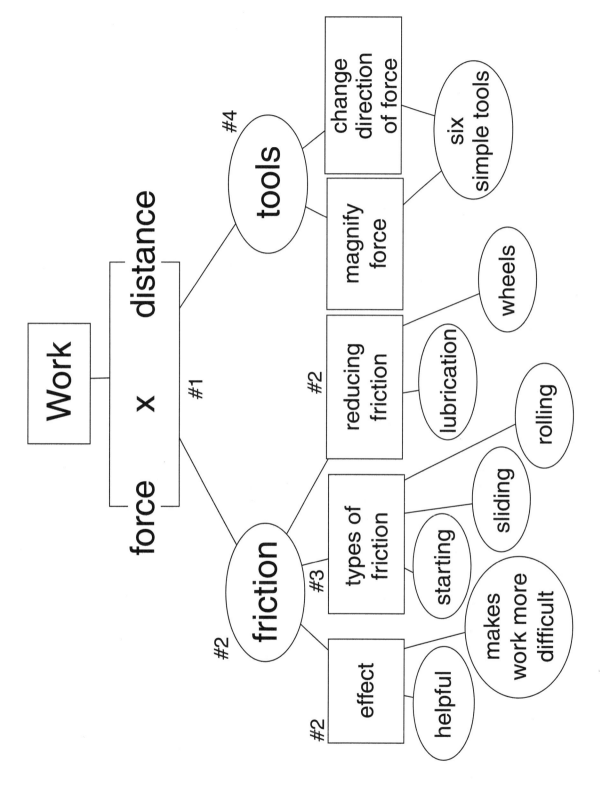

What is work?

Tool Concepts:

- Work is related to force and motion.
- For work to take place, an object, or load, must move as the result of a force acting upon it in the direction of its movement.
- Work is defined as: force x distance = work. In this formula, force is equal to the weight of the load.
- Work is increased in two ways: an increase in the weight of the load and an increase in the distance moved.

Teacher's Note: On *Lots of Science Library Book #1* page #14, the formula for work does not take into account the effect of friction on the load.

Vocabulary Words: work   force   load   distance   weight   *motion   *formula
*physics

Read: *Lots of Science Library Book #1.*

Activities:

Work – Graphic Organizer

Focus Skill: defining components
Paper Handouts: 8.5" x 11" sheet of paper   a copy of Graphics 1A–C
Graphic Organizer: Make a Hot Dog, 3 Tab Book. Draw/glue the picture for the work formula on each tab. Write/copy the formula across the top, as in the illustration below. Under each tab:

✎   Write clue words about each word in the formula: *force – push, pull; distance – inches, feet meters, miles; work – force x distance=work.* Orally review the formula.

✎✎   Complete ✎. Write a sentence, using the clue words, explaining work.

✎✎✎   Describe each component in the work formula. Determine how work can be increased an use the formula to defend the explanation.

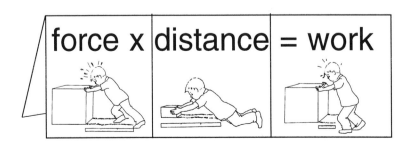

Paper Handouts: 6 sheets of 12" x 18" paper   a copy of Graphics 1D–O
     a copy of Tools in Time Graphics 1P–Q

Graphic Organizer: Make an Accordion Book with the paper. Follow the directions on page 5. Glue Graphics 1D at the middle of the first page of the Accordion Book. Glue 1E at the middle of the second page of the Accordion Book. Continue with Graphics 1F–O and the remaining pages.

Glue Tools in Time Graphics 1P and 1Q on the appropriate places in the Timeline Book. Copy the date of use on the picture. Draw a line from the graphic to the timeline and color the region where the tool was used. Add any other tools discovered in research to the Timeline Book.

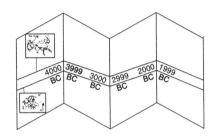

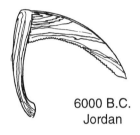

6000 B.C.
Jordan

4500 B.C.
Yugoslavia

Experiences, Investigations, and Research

Select one or more of the following activities for individual or group enrichment projects. Allow your students to determine the format in which they would like to report, share, or graphically present what they have discovered. This should be a creative investigation that utilizes your students' strengths.

 1. Make a list of the work you do in one day. Select one item on your list and describe it in individual steps, such as: pick up bowl, open cabinet, grab box, turn box to pour cereal in bowl, put box on shelf, etc.

 2. Weigh a load, move it a measured distance, and calculate the work completed with the formula. Increase the work with more weight or more distance. Calculate the work using the formula.

 3. Investigate how resistance training can strengthen muscles.

 4. Work and energy are measured in joules. Research the life of British physicist James Prescott Joule. Make a 4 Door Book. Label the tabs *Who, What, When,* and *Where.* Under each tab, write information found in the research.

What is friction?

Tool Concepts:

- Friction is a force that takes place when one surface slides against another.
- Friction is helpful to us in many ways. Friction allows us to slow down a car, grab an object, and stop when we are running.
- Friction makes work more difficult. Because of friction, we need to increase force for work to take place.
- Friction can be decreased in two ways: lubrication and wheels.

Teacher's Note: The labs for this program require the use of a force meter to quantitatively measure force needed to raise or move a load. The directions for a force meter are located in the Activity Section of this lesson. However a spring scale or fish scale may be purchased and used as a force meter for the labs. Since the force meters will be of different tensions, it is necessary for you to calibrate the meter to objects that can be used as a load in the labs.

A load can be two or more books tied together with string or a pound of flour in a secured plastic bag. To calibrate the force meter, find an object that registers a low level when being raised.

Remember the force meter is not a standardized measurement, so all labs that compare forces need to be performed with the same force meter.

Vocabulary Words: surface   friction   increase   decrease   wheels   liquid
*lubrication

Read: *Lots of Science Library Book #2.*

Activities:

Friction – Graphics Organizer

Focus Skills: acquiring information, explaining concepts
Paper Handouts: 8.5" x 11" sheet of paper   a copy of Graphics 2A–D
Graphic Organizer: Make a Small Question and Answer Book. Draw/glue Graphics 2A–D on the tabs as shown.

✎ Create friction by rubbing your hands together. Discuss it and under the first flap write/copy clue words about friction: *heat, rub surfaces.* Run and stop on tile floor to experience friction. Discuss and write/copy words about how friction helps people: *stops, holds.* Discuss with students how friction affects work and write/copy words: *makes work harder.* Discuss with students how to decrease friction and make work easier: *lubrication,* or *liquids, wheels.*

✎✎ Under the first tab, describe friction. Under the second tab, explain how friction benefits people. Under the third tab, explain how it affects work. Under the fourth tab, list two ways that friction can be reduced, making work easier to complete.

✎✎✎ Complete ✎✎. List examples under each tab to reinforce the explanations.

Investigative Loop – Experiencing Friction – Lab 2–1

Lab 2–1

Focus Skill: experiencing a concept
Lab Materials: cornmeal
Paper Handouts: 8.5" x 11" sheet of paper   a copy of Lab Graphics 2–1
       Lab Record Cards (index cards or pieces of 3" x 4" paper)
Graphic Organizer: Make a Pocket Book. See page 2 for illustrations. This is the students' Lab Book. Glue Lab Graphic 2–1 on the left pocket.
Question: What is friction?
Research: Read *Lots of Science Library Book #2*. Review friction.
Procedure: Rub your hands together. Dip your hands in cornmeal and rub them together.
Observations: Describe how your hands felt when they were rubbed together without the cornmeal. Describe how they felt when you rubbed them with the cornmeal.
Record the Data: Label two Lab Record Cards, "Lab 2–1," and the date. On one Lab Record Card, write words or phrases describing your observations of the hand–rubbing without the cornmeal. On the other Lab Record Card, describe your observations of the hand rubbing with cornmeal.
Conclusions: Review the data and draw a conclusion about the differences in your observations.
Communicate the Conclusions: Label a Lab Record Card, Lab 2–1 and the date. Write your conclusion. Store all the Lab Record Cards in the left pocket of the Lab Book.
Spark Questions: Discuss questions sparked by the lab.
New Loop: Choose a question to investigate further or complete the New Loop below.

Investigative Loop – Reducing Friction – Lab 2–2

Focus Skill: experiencing a concept
Lab Materials: lotion
Paper Handouts: Lab Book   Lab Record Cards   a copy of Lab Graphics 2–2
Graphic Organizer: Glue Lab Graphic 2–2 on the right pocket of the Lab Book.
Question: How can friction be reduced?
Research: Read *Lots of Science Library Book #2*. Review the question.
Procedure: Rub your hands together. Then put lotion on your hands and rub them together.
Observations: Describe how your hands felt when they were rubbed together without the lotion. How did they feel when you rubbed them with the lotion?
Record the Data: Label two Lab Record Cards "Lab 2–2," and the date. Write words or phrases that describe your observations without and with the lotion on your hands.
Conclusions: Review the data. Draw conclusions about the difference in your observations.
Communicate the Conclusions: Review the data and draw a conclusion about the differences in your observations. Label a Lab Record Card, "Lab 2–2," and write your conclusion. Store all the Lab Record Cards in the right pocket of the Lab Book.
Spark Questions: Discuss questions sparked by the lab.
New Loop: Choose a question to investigate further.
✎✎✎ **Design Your Own Experiment:** Select a topic based upon the experiences in these *Investigative Loops*. see page viii for more details.

Force Meter

Focus Skills: following directions, measurements

Activity Materials: piece of wood (approximately 3" x 10")   rubber band   12" piece of string
    tack   two U–shaped nails   bead that will be held securely on the string
    paper clip   metric ruler   piece of paper   hammer

Activity: Follow the directions below to make a force meter.

1. Tie one end of the string to the rubber band, using several knots.
2. Tack the rubber band to the end of the wood.
3. Hammer a U–shaped nail just under the rubber band and string connection, in line wit the tack.
4. Thread the string through the bead and slide the bead to the rubber band.
5. Hammer a U–shaped nail at the other end of the wood, over the string.
6. Tie the paper clip to the string.
7. Cut the paper to fit on the wood, to the left of the string. Make the paper long enough to fit in-between the two U–shaped nails.
8. Use the ruler to make cm lines and label them 0, 1, 2, 3, etc. Glue the paper so that the bead is on the zero mark.
9. Attach the load to the paper clip and hold the wood as you pull. The bead will indicate the amount of force used to move the load. Reset the bead at zero before each pull.
10. Calibrate the force meter before it is used in the *Investigative Loops*. See the Teacher's Note in this lesson.

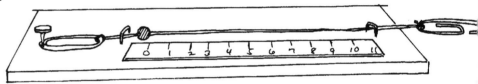

Tools in Time – Timeline Book

Paper Handouts: Timeline Book   a copy of Graphics 2E–F

Graphic Organizer: Glue Graphics 2E and F to the appropriate places in the Timeline Book. Copy the date for use on the picture. Draw a line from the graphic to the timeline and color the region where the tool was used. Add any other tools discovered in research to the Timeline Book.

700 B.C.
Europe

6000 B.C.
France

xperiences, Investigations, and Research

elect one or more of the following activities for individual or group enrichment projects. Allow our students to determine the format in which they would like to report, share, or graphically resent what they have discovered. This should be a creative investigation that utilizes your tudents' strengths.

 1. List the positive and negative effects of friction on daily life.

 2. About 20% of a car engine's power is used to overcome friction. Find out how much power is used to overcome friction in several other common machines. Graph your information.

 3. Explain the following: *Because friction changes some machine energy to heat, the amount of output work is always less than the amount of input work.*

 4. Research the cosmetic use of exfoliates and explain how exfoliates rely upon friction to work.

http://web.mit.edu/invent

What are the types of friction?

Tool Concepts:

- Friction is greatest just before an object moves. This is called starting friction.
- Friction lessens when an object is in motion. This is called sliding friction.
- Friction lessens when an object rolls on wheels. This is called rolling friction.
- The amount of friction depends upon the amount of force between the two objects or surfaces. Therefore, heavier objects create more friction when being moved and lighter objects create less friction when being moved.

Teacher's Note: An alternative assessment suggestion for this lesson is found on pages 72–73. If Graphic Pages are being consumed, first photocopy assessment graphics that are needed .

Vocabulary Words: starting friction   sliding friction   rolling friction

Read: *Lots of Science Library Book #3.*

Activities:

Types of Friction – Graphic Organizer

Focus Skills: comparing and contrasting, describing concepts
Materials: 8.5" x 11" sheet of paper   a copy of Graphics 3A–C
Graphic Organizer: Make a Hot Dog, 3 Tab Book. On each tab, draw/glue Graphics 3A–C and label each tab.

   ✎ Under each tab, write/dictate clue words about the amount of friction in each situation: *most friction, less friction, least friction.*

   ✎✎ Explain each type of friction under the appropriate tab and give common examples of each. Compare and contrast the amount of friction produced in each situation.

starting friction   sliding friction   rolling friction

   ✎✎✎ Complete ✎✎. Research these types of friction and record the data under the appropriate tab.

Investigative Loop – Compare Types of Friction – Lab 3–1

Teacher's Note: For the load in this lab, use books large enough to register on your force meter.
Focus Skills: measuring force, compare and contrast
Lab Materials: 3 yards of string   books used as a load   force meter
Paper Handouts: 8.5" x 11" sheet of paper   Lab Record Cards   Lab Book
     a copy of Lab Graphics 3–1
Graphic Organizer: Make a Pocket Book. Glue it side–by–side to the Lab Book. Glue Lab Graphic 3–1 on the left pocket of the Lab Book.

Question: How does friction affect the amount of force needed to move an object?

Research: Read *Lots of Science Library Book #3*. Review starting, sliding, and rolling friction.

Lab 3–1

Prediction: Predict the amount of force needed for each type of movement: starting, sliding, and rolling. "The starting movement will take more or less force than…"

Procedure: Place the books in a stack. Tie string around them to hold them in place. Attach a pulling string to it. Attach a force meter to the pulling string and pull the books, sliding them for several feet. Put the books on wheels or use several round pencils or pens to simulate wheels and pull them using the same method. If using pencils, ask one person to move the pencils from the back to the front of the books as they move.

Observations: Observe the force meter when the books start to move, when they are sliding, and when they are rolling.

Record the Data: Label three Lab Record Cards, "Lab 3–1," the date, and the type of action: starting, sliding, rolling. On each Lab Record Card, record the force measurements of each action.

Conclusions: Review the data collected. Compare the force needed to start the books moving to the force needed to keep them sliding, and to the force needed to move the books on wheels. Since the weight of the books is the same, the difference in the amount of force needed is a result of friction.

Communicate the Conclusions: Report the data on a bar graph. Explain the graph to one person who did not participate in the lab.

Spark Questions: Discuss questions sparked by the lab.

New Loop: Investigate one question further or create a New Loop using the above procedure on different surfaces: carpet, concrete, or tile.

✎✎✎ **Design Your Own Experiment:** Select a topic based upon this *Investigative Loop* experience. See page viii for more details.

Investigative Loop – The Race – Lab 3–2

Focus Skills: predicting outcome, drawing conclusions

Lab Materials: ice cube   toy car   eraser   board or large book

Paper Handouts: Lab Book   Lab Record Cards   a copy of Lab Graphics 3–2

Graphic Organizer: Glue Lab Graphics 3–2 on the right pocket.

Question: Which object will move faster, and why?

Research: Read *Lots of Science Library Book #3* and review friction.

Lab 3–2

Predictions: Predict which object will move the fastest on a board or book. "The ____ will move the fastest." Write the prediction on a Lab Record Card labeled "Lab 3–2."

Procedure: Put the board or large book on a stair or stack of books. Assign three people to hold an object in place at the top of the board. Instruct the holders to let go at the same time.

Observations: Watch the race. Which object reached the bottom of the board first? Second? Last?

Record the Data: Label a Lab Record Card "Lab 3–2," the date, and the first, second, and third place holders of the race. Record any other observations made during the race. Store cards in the appropriate pocket of the Lab Book.

Conclusions: Review the data. Draw conclusions about the order of the race.

Communicate the Conclusions: On a Lab Record Card, explain the conclusion. Option: Make a Half Book and write a newspaper article about this great race.

Spark Questions: Discuss questions sparked by the lab.

New Loop: Investigate one question further.

✎✎✎ **Design Your Own Experiment:** Select a topic based upon this *Investigative Loop* experience. See page viii for more details.

Paper Handouts: Timeline Book   a copy of Graphic 3D
Graphic Organizer: Glue Graphic 3D to the appropriate place in the
   Timeline Book. Copy the date of use on the picture. Draw a
   line from the graphic to the timeline and color the region where the
   tool was used. Add any other tools discovered in research to the
   Timeline Book.

1000 B.C.
Northern Europe

Experiences, Investigations, and Research

Select one or more of the following activities for individual or group enrichment projects. Allow your students to determine the format in which they would like to report, share, or graphically present what they have discovered. This should be a creative investigation that utilizes your students' strengths.

 1. Using the Procedure in Lab 3–1, predict how changes will affect the forces needed to move the book. Put a large book on the bottom of the stack, then put a small book on the bottom of the stack. Measure the forces on the differently arranged stacks of books. Compare the results to your predictions. Can you make a generalization about the force needed for different types of loads?

 2. Read a biography on one of the following:
Isaac Newton
Leonardo da Vinci
Benjamin Franklin
James Watt
Michael Faraday
Thomas Edison
Alexander Graham Bell
The Wright Brothers
Make a 4 Door Book to report the *Who, What, When,* and *Where* of the inventor's life.

 4. Explain the part friction plays in the following activities: ice skating, roller blading, sledding, and snow boarding.

 3. Make a hovercraft. Cut off the top of a plastic bottle with scissors. Drill a small hole in the cap. Blow up a balloon and stretch it over the bottle cap. Push the hovercraft gently and it should glide. The cushion of air acts as a lubricant and reduces friction.

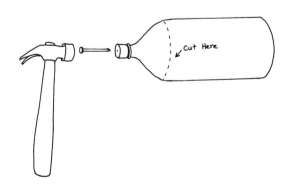

Tools Concept Map
Lessons 4–24
Numbers Refer to Lesson Numbers

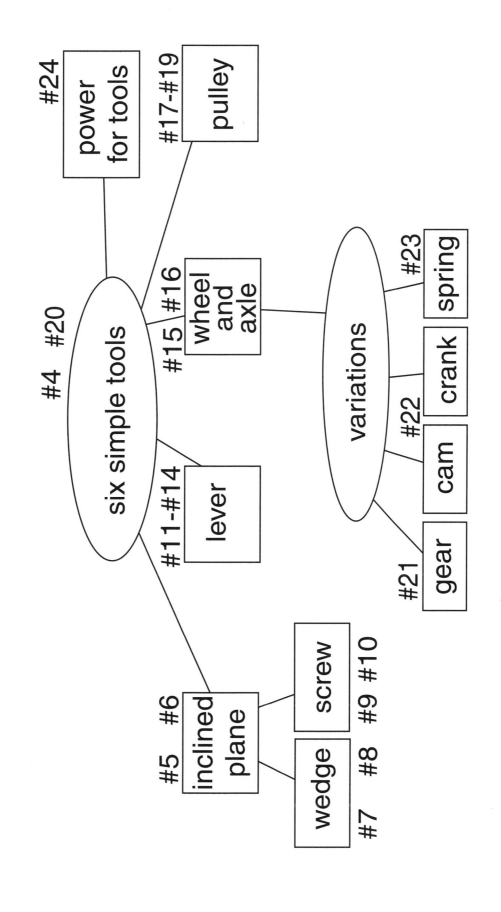

What is a tool?

Tool Concepts:

- Tools make work easier because they change the force applied to the work.
- Tools magnify force and alter the direction of the force.
- With tools we can do work with less force, or effort.
- There are six basic tools: inclined plane, wedge, screw, lever, wheel and axle, and pulley.

Vocabulary Words: tool   machine   effort   magnify   direction
*mechanical advantage   *complex machine   *input force   *output force

Teacher's Note: This lesson begins the Technology Unit. Students completing this unit can make a Bound Book out of 8 pieces of paper. (See page 4 for instructions). Activities for the Technology Unit are found after the *Experiences, Investigations, and Research* sections of each lesson. Pictures for the activities are found on the Technology Graphics Pages following Graphics Page 24.

Read: *Lots of Science Library Book #4.*

Activities:

Investigative Loop – How to Magnify Force – Lab 4–1

Focus Skills: experiencing a concept, observing
Lab Materials: two broomsticks   a long rope   three people
Paper Handouts: 8.5" x 11" sheet of paper   Lab Book   Lab Record Cards
          a copy of Lab Graphics 4–1
Graphic Organizer: Make a Pocket Book and glue it side–by–side to the Lab Book. Glue Lab
          Graphic 4–1 on the left pocket.
Concept: Tools make work easier.
Research: Read *Lots of Science Library Book #4* and review tools.
Procedure: Wrap a rope around the two broomsticks as shown.
          One person will hold one broomstick and another person will hold the other one.
          Throughout the lab they are to pull on the broomsticks in a firm and consistent manner,
          but not with all their strength to keep the broomsticks apart. The third person is the
          worker. First, the worker will try to move the broomsticks together by pulling
          them. Then the worker will try to accomplish the same job by pulling on the
          rope end, as shown
Observations: What happened when the worker tried to pull the broomsticks
          together? What happened when the worker pulled on the rope?
Record the Data: Label a Lab Record Card, "Lab 4–1," the date, and a description of this lab.
          Describe the results of each type of work.

Conclusions: How do you explain the difference in results? The rope is a tool. What difference did the tool make in the work being completed?

Communicate the Conclusions: On a Lab Record Card, explain your conclusions and the power of the tool, or rope.

Spark Questions: Discuss questions sparked by this lab.

New Loop: Choose one question to investigate further.

✎✎✎ **Design Your Own Experiment:** Select a topic based upon this *Investigative Loop* experience. See page viii for more details.

A Tool Sign – Graphic Organizer

Paper Handouts: 2 sheets of 8.5" x 11" paper   a copy of Graphics 4A

Graphic Organizer: Make a Layered Look Book. On the front cover draw/glue the special "tools" word and finish the sentence "Tools make work easier." Cut in the center through the bottom three pages. Label each tab with the name of a simple tool.

Teacher's Note: Store this book for future use.

TOOLS make work easier	
inclined plane	wedge
screw	lever
wheel and axle	pulley

Tools in Time – Timeline Book

Paper Handouts: Timeline Book   a copy of Graphics 4B

Graphic Organizer: Glue Graphic 4B on the appropriate place in the Timeline Book. Copy the date of use on the picture. Draw a line from the graphic to the timeline and color the region where the tool was used. Add any other tools discovered in research to the Timeline Book.

250 A.D. Roman Empire

Experiences, Investigations, and Research

Select one or more of the following activities for individual or group enrichment projects. Allow your students to determine the format in which they would like to report, share, or graphically present what they have discovered. This should be a creative investigation that utilizes your students' strengths.

1. Make a list of the tools that you use in one day. Next to each tool, write the work that the tool helps you to complete.

2. Read this list of jobs and decide what tool would help you to do each job.
   a) dig a hole   b) slice bread   c) fix a hinge on a door
   d) trim bushes   e) paint a room   f) attach papers together

3. Research why machines were developed to fight battles. Find specific examples of how advancements in battle machinery changed history.

Technology – Interview several people of various ages and find out what they consider to be the greatest technological advancement or feat in their lifetime. Record the answers in your Technology Bound Book. Compare the answers for similarities and differences.

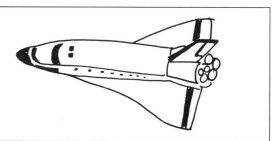

What is an inclined plane?

Tool Concepts:

- An inclined plane is a simple tool.
- An inclined plane is a slanted surface used to raise a load.
- An inclined plane magnifies force.

Vocabulary Words: inclined plane   slanted

Read: *Lots of Science Library Book #5.*

Activities:

The Inclined Plane – Graphic Organizer

Focus Skills: describing a tool, explaining forces
Paper Handouts: 8.5" x 11" sheet of paper   a copy of Graphics 5A–B
Graphic Organizer: Make a Large Question and Answer Book. On the cover, draw/glue Graphic 5A and write/copy the tool name. Open the Large Question and Answer Book. On the first tab, draw/glue Graphic 5B, and title it *The Tool*. Under the tab:

✎ Draw an inclined plane. Draw a load on the inclined plane. Draw arrows showing the direction that the load moves on the tool. Arrows should go up and down on the inclined plane.

✎✎ Describe an inclined plane. Explain how it is used and how it magnifies force.

✎✎✎ Complete ✎✎. Include information on and examples of ways to reduce friction when using this tool.

Teacher's Note: Store this book for Lesson 6.

A Tool Sign

Focus Skill: application of information
Paper Handouts: The Tool Layered Look Book made in Lesson 4
Graphic Organizer: On the page titled *inclined plane,* list some inclined planes found around you.

make work easie

inclined plane	wedge
screw	lever
wheel and axle	pulley

Paper Handouts: Timeline Book   a copy of Graphics 5C
Graphic Organizer: Glue Graphic 5C to the appropriate place in the Timeline Book. Copy the date of use on the picture. Draw a line from the graphic to the timeline and color the region where the tool was used. Add any other tools discovered in research to the Timeline Book.

Experiences, Investigations, and Research

Select one or more of the following activities for individual or group enrichment projects. Allow your students to determine the format in which they would like to report, share, or graphically present what they have discovered. This should be a creative investigation that utilizes your students' strengths.

6000 B.C.
Jericho

   1. Investigate how ancient Egyptians built the pyramids. Although we do not know for sure how these huge structures were built, the inclined plane probably played a large role in the process. Speculate how the inclined plane could have helped in building these structures. Draw pictures to illustrate your ideas. Research current theories and compare and contrast them to your own.

2. Describe stairs as inclined planes. Measure the height of several sets of stairs and record the measurements. Does there seem to be a standard measurement for stairs? Explain.

3. Use the following to record quantitative observations: *It takes ___(number) stairs, each _____ (inches/cm) high to reach a level of ____ (feet/meters) above the ground.*

4. Explain why mountain trails and steep staircases are seldom straight paths.

Technology – Glass is a material made from sand, soda, and limestone. Research how glass is made, molded, and why it is such a valuable material.

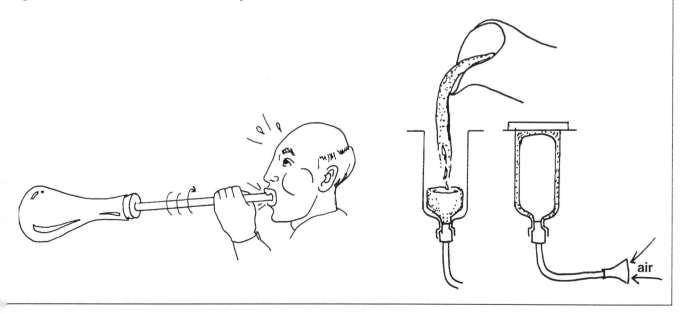

How do we use inclined planes?

Tool Concepts:

- An inclined plane spreads out force over a longer distance.
- An inclined plane gives the worker a mechanical advantage.
- A mechanical advantage means the tool allows more work to be done with less effort.
- A longer board at the same height gives the worker a greater mechanical advantage.
- Friction takes place when using an inclined plane.

Vocabulary Words: board   direction

Read: *Lots of Science Library Book #6.*

Activities:

The Tool | The Tool at work

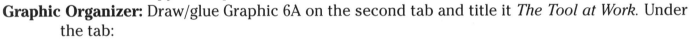
Inclined Planes – Graphic Organizer

Focus Skill: application of information
Paper Handouts: Inclined Plane Large Question and Answer Book from Lesson 6
    a copy of Graphic 6A
Graphic Organizer: Draw/glue Graphic 6A on the second tab and title it *The Tool at Work.* Under the tab:
- ✎ Write/copy the list of examples found on the front tab.
- ✎✎ Name each example found on the front tab. Explain where each is found.
- ✎✎✎ Name each example found on the front tab. Explain where each example is found and how it makes work easier.

Investigative Loop – Work and the Inclined Plane Lab 6–1

Focus Skills: measuring force, comparing and contrasting
Lab Materials: 3 yards of string   a board or large book   load used in Lab 3-
    a longer board or larger book   a force meter
Paper Handouts: 8.5" x 11" sheet of paper   a copy of Graphics 6B–E   Lab Book
    a copy of Lab Graphic 6–1
Graphic Organizer: Make a Small Question and
    Answer Book. Draw/glue the lab pictures on
    each tab as shown.
    Glue Lab Graphic 6–1 to the right pocket
    of the Lab Book.

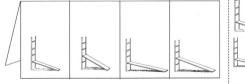
Lab 6–1

Question: How does the length and height of a ramp affect the amount of force needed to raise a load?

Research: Read *Lots of Science Library Book #6* and review the question listed above.

Prediction: Predict how different lengths and heights of a ramp will affect the force needed to raise a load. "The longer the ramp the .... force is needed to lift the load. The higher the ramp..."

Procedure: Tie a string around the books. Tie another string to that one so that the books can be pulled with the spring balance or force meter. Use the shorter board or book as a ramp placed at a lower level on a stair or stack of books. Pull the books up the ramp. Place the same ramp at a higher level and complete the same procedure. Now take the longer board or larger book, and place it at the lower level used in the first pull. Raise this longer ramp to the higher level and complete the same procedure.

Observations: Observe the force meter as the books are moved up each ramp.

Record the Data: Under each tab, record the amount of force needed to raise the books.

Conclusions: Compare the amount of force needed to complete each job in the lab. Which inclined plane required the most force to raise the load? Which one required the least amount of force? Use the force numbers to determine which inclined plane made work the easiest and why. Compare the conclusions with the predictions.

Communicate the Conclusions: Explain the conclusions on the back of the Inclined Plane Small Question and Answer Book. Share this book with two people in the next 24 hours. Show each person the pictures on the front and ask them to make predictions about the force needed for each job. Fold the book and put it in the Lab Book for Lab 6–1.

Spark Questions: Discuss questions sparked by this lab.

New Loop: Choose one question to investigate further.

✏✏✏ **Design Your Own Experiment:** Select a topic based upon this *Investigative Loop* Experience.

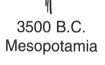

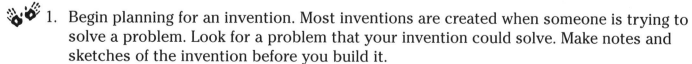

Tools in Time – Timeline Book

Paper Handouts: Timeline Book   a copy of Graphic 6F

Graphic Organizer: Glue Graphic 6F to the appropriate place in the Timeline Book. Copy the date of use on the picture. Draw a line from the graphic to the timeline and color the region where the tool was used. Add any other tools discovered in research to the Timeline Book.

3500 B.C.
Mesopotamia

Experiences, Investigations, and Research

Select one or more of the following activities for individual or group enrichment projects. Allow your students to determine the format in which they would like to report, share, or graphically present what they have discovered. This should be a creative investigation that utilizes your students' strengths.

1. Begin planning for an invention. Most inventions are created when someone is trying to solve a problem. Look for a problem that your invention could solve. Make notes and sketches of the invention before you build it.

2. Investigate the use of inclined planes in building codes for handicapped access. What angles are used for these ramp constructions, and why?

Technology – The most common technique for molding plastic is injection molding, in which molten plastic is forced into closed steel molds. A Lego™ or other plastic toy is a good example of something made with injection molding. Research injection molding and locate information on the process of making such plastic items.

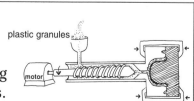

plastic granules

motor

Great Science Adventures

Lesson 7

What is a wedge?

Tool Concepts:

- A wedge is a simple tool. It has a thick end that tapers into a thin, pointed end.
- When force is applied to the thick end of a wedge such as a doorstop, the force is magnified to go under or into an object.
- Applied force to a wedge is also converted into a sideways motion and is used to push or break an object apart, as in the case of an axe.
- A wedge is an inclined plane.

Vocabulary Words: wedge   thick   thin   pointed   tapers   *resistant

Read: *Lots of Science Library Book #7.*

wedge

Activities:

What is a Wedge? – Graphic Organizer

Focus Skills: explaining how a wedge magnifies force, describing a tool
Paper Handouts: 8.5" x 11" sheet of paper   a copy of Graphics 7A–B
Graphic Organizer: Make a Large Question and Answer Book. Draw/glue Graphic 7A on the cover and write/copy the name of the tool. Open the Large Question and Answer Book. On the first tab, draw/glue Graphic 7B and write *The Tool.* Under the tab:

The Tool

input force → output forces

- ✎ Draw a wedge. Write/copy the names of each part of the wedge: *thick end; thin, pointed end.* Draw a black arrow to show where the force is applied to the tool. Draw blue arrows to show how the tool uses that force.
- ✎✎ Explain how this wedge magnifies force and converts the direction of the force.
- ✎✎✎ Complete ✎✎. Describe in detail the "pulling apart" force that wedges use in work.

A Tool Sign

Focus Skill: application of information
Paper Handouts: The Tool Layered Look Book made in Lesson 4
    On the page titled *wedge,* list wedges that you see around you.

make work easi

inclined plane	wedge
screw	lever
wheel and axle	pulley

Focus Skill: following directions
Paper Handouts: a copy of Graphics 7C–D   thin cardboard (from a cereal box or poster board)
   Read the directions aloud or ask your students to read them silently. As each step is
   completed, check the box next to it. When the wedge is completed, discuss the parts and
   uses of this tool.

Tools in Time – Timeline Book

Paper Handouts: Timeline Book   a copy of Graphics 7E
Graphic Organizer: Glue Graphics 7E to the appropriate place in the Timeline
   Book. Draw a line from the graphic to the timeline and color the
   country where the tool was used. Add any other tools discovered
   in research to the Timeline Book.

400 B.C.
China

Experiences, Investigations, and Research

Select one or more of the following activities for individual or group enrichment projects. Allow
your students to determine the format in which they would like to report, share, or graphically
present what they have discovered. This should be a creative investigation that utilizes your
students' strengths.

 1 Look through *The Way Things Work* by David Macaulay. Find several interesting
      sections to read and share with someone else.

 2. Explain why a wedge is a moving form of an inclined plane.

 3. List examples of wedges that have one sloping side, such as a doorstop. List wedges
      with two sloping sides, such as an axe.

http://www.
indirect.com/
www/dhixson/
machines.html

Technology – Cutting materials have progressed from stone axes to metal tools
to lasers used in surgery. Investigate cutting tools through the timeline of
technology and report your findings.

How do we use wedges?

Tool Concepts:

- Wedges are used every day. Some common wedges are knives, scissors, and doorstops.
- A plow uses a group of wedges to create furrows in soil.
- A zipper is opened and closed with sets of wedges. Inside the slide of a zipper is a triangular wedge that opens the zipper and a set of two curved wedges that close the zipper.

Vocabulary Words: plow   zipper   slide   *titanium

Read: *Lots of Science Library Book #8.*

Activities:

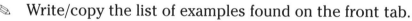

Wedges We Use – Graphic Organizer

Focus Skill: application of information
Paper Handouts: Wedge Large Question and Answer Book from Lesson 7
    a copy of Graphic 8A
Graphic Organizer: Draw/glue Graphic 8A on the second tab. Write *The Tool at Work*. Under the tab:

  ✎ Write/copy the list of examples found on the front tab.

  ✎✎ Name each example found on the front tab. Explain how each example is a wedge.

  ✎✎✎ Name each example found on the front tab. Explain how each example is a wedge and how it makes work easier.

The Most Useful Wedges – Graphic Organizer

Focus Skills: research, labeling parts
Paper Handouts: 8.5" x 11" sheet of paper   a copy of Graphics 8B or 8C
Graphic Organizer: Make a Half Book. On the cover, draw/glue either Graphic 8B or 8C and title the book. Inside:

  ✎ Draw an illustration of a plow or zipper. Draw arrows to show how the tool uses the forces of the wedge.

  ✎✎ Research the tool you chose for this book. Illustrate the tool and label all its parts. Explain how the tool is used and the usefulness of the wedges in it.

  ✎✎✎ Complete ✎✎. Incorporate historical information about the tool in your explanation.

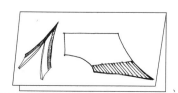
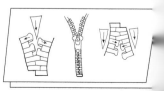

aper Handouts: Timeline Book   a copy of Graphics 8D–E

raphic Organizer: Glue Graphics 8D–E to the appropriate places in the Timeline Book. Copy the date of use on the picture. Draw a line from the graphic to the timeline and color the region where the tool was used. Add any other tools discovered in research to the Timeline Book.

3000 B.C.
Egypt

1000 B.C.
Europe/Asia

xperiences, Investigations, and Research

elect one or more of the following activities for individual or group enrichment projects. Allow our students to determine the format in which they would like to report, share, or graphically resent what they have discovered. This should be a creative investigation that utilizes your tudents' strengths.

 1. The zipper was first displayed to the public at the 1893 World's Fair in Chicago. It was largely ignored by the people of that time. Research how clothes were fastened before zippers.

 2. Research the use of wedges as weapons since prehistoric times.

 3. Research the use of wedges in quarrying from prehistoric times to present.

 4. Investigate woodworkers' tools and their use of wedges to shape and form wood. Include the carpenter's plane in the investigation.

Technology – The aristocratic Japanese warriors known as the samurai needed the finest of swords. Hard steels containing large amounts of carbon were hammered onto a core of soft, low carbon iron to produce a weapon that would stay sharp but not break in combat. Investigate the use of swords throughout the ages and cultures. Report your findings.

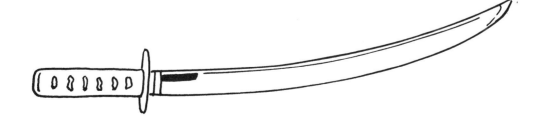

Great Science Adventures

What is a screw?

Tool Concepts:

- A screw is a simple tool made from an inclined plane wrapped around a cylinder.
- The spiral around the screw is called the thread.
- The distance between the threads is the pitch of the screw.
- A screw will magnify the turning force applied to its top.
- A screw must be turned many times to move the screw a short distance.

Vocabulary Words: screw   attach   cylinder   *thread   *pitch   *cast *foundry

Read: *Lots of Science Library Book #9.*

Activities:

What is a Screw? – Graphic Organizer

Focus Skills: labeling parts, explaining force

Paper Handouts: 8.5" x 11" sheet of paper   a copy of Graphics 9A–B

Graphic Organizer: Make a Large Question and Answer Book. Draw/glue Graphic 9A on the cover and write/copy the name of the tool. Open the book. On the first tab, draw/glue Graphic 9B and write *The Tool*. Under the tab:

✎ Draw a screw. Write/copy the names of the parts of the screw. Use black arrows to show how force is applied to the screw. Use blue arrows to show how the screw uses that force.

✎✎ Draw a screw. Label its parts. Explain how a screw magnifies force.

✎✎✎ Complete ✎✎. After the "Make a Screw" activity, which follows, is completed, record the data in this book.

A Tool Sign

Focus Skill: application of information

Paper Handouts: The Tool Layered Look Book made in Lesson 4

On the page titled *screw,* list the screws that you see around you.

make work easi	
inclined plane	wedge
screw	lever
wheel and axle	pulley

Make a Screw

Focus Skill: following directions
Paper Handouts: a copy of graphics 9C–E
    Read the directions aloud or ask your students to read them silently. As each direction is completed, check the box next to it. When the tool is completed, discuss the parts it uses.
 Using the Ideal Mechanical Advantage formula, determine the Mechanical Advantage of this screw.

Experience a Screwdriver

Focus Skill: discovering a concept.
Activity Materials: screw   screwdriver   a piece of wood
Activity: Start the screw in the wood. Ask your students to continue screwing it in. Observe the amount of force needed to move the screw.

Tools in Time – Timeline Book

Paper Handouts: Timeline Book   a copy of Graphics 9F–G
Graphic Organizer: Glue Graphics 9F–G to the appropriate places in the Timeline Book. Copy the date of use on the picture. Draw a line from the graphic to the timeline and color the region where the tool was used. Add any other tools discovered in research to the Timeline Book.

1450 B.C.   1405 A.D.
Mesopotamia   Europe

xperiences, Investigations, and Research

Select one or more of the following activities for individual or group enrichment projects. Allow your students to determine the format in which they would like to report, share, or graphically present what they have discovered. This should be a creative investigation that utilizes your students' strengths.

 1. Continue working on the invention you began in Lesson 6.

2. Investigate the Greek mathematician Apollonius of Perga. Explain how his work with the geometry of the spiral helix led to the development of the screw.

Technology – The aluminum can is an ingenious piece of technology. A modern aluminum can has 30% less metal than one made 20 years ago. Aluminum cans are lightweight, yet strong enough to hold many items. Recycling of aluminum cans now take place worldwide. Investigate aluminum and learn the process involved in making these useful byproducts of technology.

Technology – Before aluminum cans were used as widely as they are today, most sodas were sold in bottles. Interview someone or research to find out if and how these bottles were "recycled."

Great Science Adventures

How do we use screws?

Tool Concepts:

- Screws are used in many tools: a water faucet, a drill, nuts and bolts, a corkscrew, and a vice
- Archimedes' screw consisted of a large continuous screw inside a cylinder. The lower end wa placed in the river and as the spiral threads were turned, the water was raised.
- Other uses of Archimedes' screw are found in a meat grinder and a combine harvester.

Teacher's Note: An alternative assessment suggestion for this lesson is found on pages 72–73. If Graphic Pages are being consumed, first photocopy assessment graphics that are needed.

Vocabulary Words: faucet   drill   vice   nuts   bolts   *complicated

Read: *Lots of Science Library Book #10.*

Activities:

Screws We Use – Graphic Organizer

Focus Skill: applying information
Paper Handouts: Large Question and Answer Book made in Lesson 9
    a copy of Graphics 10A
Graphic Organizer: Draw/glue Graphic 10A on the second tab of
    the book and write *The Tool at Work.* Under the tab:
✎   Write/copy the name of these tools.
✎✎   Explain how the screw in each tool makes work easier to complete.
✎✎✎   Explain how these tools are used and how they help the worker.

Tools in Time – Timeline Book

Paper Handouts: Timeline Book   a copy of Graphics 10B–C
Graphic Organizer: Glue Graphics 10B–C to the appropriate places in the Timeline Book. Copy th date of use on the picture. Draw a line from the graphic to the timeline and color the region where the tool was used. Add any other tools discovered in research to the Timeline Book.

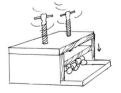

150 B.C.
Greece

1250 A.D.
France

Experiences, Investigations, and Research

Select one or more of the following activities for individual or group enrichment projects. Allow your students to determine the format in which they would like to report, share, or graphically present what they have discovered. This should be a creative investigation that utilizes your students' strengths.

 1. Make a flower or plant press with 2 nuts and bolts and heavy cardboard. Cut the cardboard into two identical rectangles. In two opposite corners, punch or drill holes large enough for the bolts to go through and still hold tightly. Lay flowers or plants between the cardboard pieces and make them as flat as possible. Screw the bolts tightly, but not to the point of distorting the cardboard. Check your plants in 5 days.

 2. Explain how a screw can be used to raise heavy objects.

 3. List examples of screws that are used to press or fasten objects, such as a bolt.

 4. Describe a ship's propeller as a screw.

 5. Explain a screw as a moving inclined plane.

 6. Investigate the history of screw jars. Add the information to the *Tools in Time* Timeline Book.

Technology – There are five methods of joining materials together:
1) fastened with a rivet, bolt, or thread
2) joined with an adhesive or solder
3) flowing together, as in welding
4) gripped with friction, as with a nail
5) shaped to lock together, such as a plastic toy.
   Research the technological advances in these fastening techniques. Report your findings.

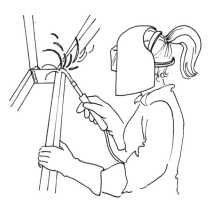
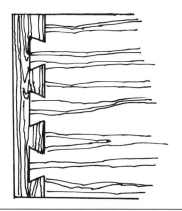

What is a lever?

Tool Concepts:

- A lever is a simple tool.
- A lever has two parts, a bar and a fulcrum. The bar or rod moves when doing work and the fulcrum does not move.
- Even though the fulcrum does not move, the bar can rotate on it to transfer force.
- A lever magnifies the force of the effort.

Vocabulary Words: rotate   lever   fulcrum   bar   rod   *fixed point   *pivot-poin

Read: *Lots of Science Library Book #11.*

Activities:

What is a Lever? – Graphic Organizer

Focus Skills: functions of a component, explaining a concept

Paper Handouts: 8.5" x 11" sheet of paper   a copy of Graphics 11A–B

Graphic Organizer: Make a Large Question and Answer Book. Draw/glue Graphic 11A and write *levers* on the cover. Open the Book. On the first tab, draw/glue Graphic 11B and write *lever* at the top.

✎ Explain the function of each part of a lever with clue words: *rod moves, fulcrum does not move.*

✎✎ Explain how the lever magnifies force and changes the direction of the force. Include information about each part of the tool.

✎✎✎ Complete ✎✎. Explain how the rotating ability of the rod impacts the advantage of the lever.

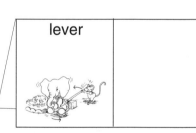

A Tool Sign

Focus Skill: application of information

Paper Handouts: The Tool Layered Look Book made in Lesson 4

On the page titled *lever,* list levers that you see around you.

inclined plane	wedge
screw	lever
wheel and axle	pulley

make work eas

Make a Lever

Focus Skill: following directions
Paper Handouts: a copy of Graphics 11C–E   thin cardboard (cereal box or poster board)
Read the directions aloud or ask your students to read them silently. As each direction is completed, check the box next to it. When the tool is completed, discuss the parts and its uses.

Experience a Lever

Focus Skill: experiencing a concept
Activity Materials: a rod   brick or stack of books to use as a fulcrum   a rock or other load
Create a lever and use it to lift a load. Observe and discuss the power of a lever. Find another object to use as the load. Predict how much effort it will require to move this load, using the lever.

Tools in Time – Timeline Book

Paper Handouts: Timeline Book   a copy of Graphics 11F–G
Graphic Organizer: Glue Graphics 11F–G to the appropriate places in the Timeline Book. Copy the date of use on each picture. Draw a line from the graphic to the timeline and color the region where the tool was used. Add any other tools discovered in research to the Timeline Book.

1500 B.C.
Egypt

1650 B.C.
Greece

Experiences, Investigations, and Research

Select one or more of the following activities for individual or group enrichment projects. Allow your students to determine the format in which they would like to report, share, or graphically present what they have discovered. This should be a creative investigation that utilizes your students' strengths.

 1. Investigate the use of levers such as poles, paddles, and oars in early water navigation. Explain how ancient civilizations used galleys, powered by many oars for transporting and warfare in the Mediterranean.

2. Call for an entry form for the Young Inventors Awards Program, 888–494–4994.

Technology – Investigate the construction of a large structure. Research the technological advances that made this feat possible. Structures to research: cathedrals, suspension bridges, skyscrapers, or dams.

Technology – Compare large structures constructed in the past to modern ones. Include information on construction methods as well as descriptions of the finished products.

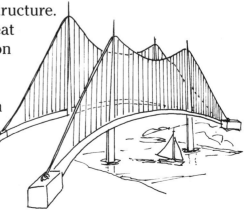

What is a class one lever?

Tool Concepts:

- Class one levers consist of a rod, fulcrum, load arm, and effort arm.
- The fulcrum divides the lever into two sides. One side holds a load. This is called the load arm.
- Force is applied to the other side of the fulcrum. This side is called the effort arm.
- If the fulcrum is moved closer to the load, or the load moves closer to the fulcrum, the amount of force needed to lift the load is decreased.
- Class one levers include the seesaw, balance scale, boat oar, pliers, and scissors.

Vocabulary Words: class one lever   seesaw   load   *measurements   *accurate

Read: *Lots of Science Library Book #12.*

Activities:

Class One Levers – Graphic Organizer

Focus Skills: labeling parts, explaining forces
Paper Handouts: Large Question and Answer Book from Lesson 11
    a copy of Graphics 12A–B
Graphic Organizer: On the second tab of the Lever Book, draw/glue Graphics 12A. Write/copy *class one lever* on the top of the tab. Under the tab, draw/glue Graphic 12B.

✎ Write/copy the names of the parts of the lever. Draw a black arrow showing where the force, or effort, is applied to this lever. This is called the input force. Draw a blue arrow showing where the force of the lever works, or the output force.

✎✎ Label the parts of the lever and list the examples shown on the tab. Explain the load arm and the effort arm of the lever.

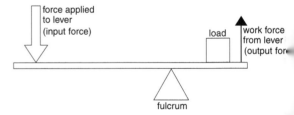

✎✎✎ Complete ✎✎. Explain output force and how to change the amount of output force with this lever.

Make a Lab Lever

Focus Skill: following directions
Activity Materials: 5/8" x 48" wooden dowel   ruler   pencil   5 small rubber band
    knife/scissors   dirt   2-liter plastic soda bottle

Activity: Use the ruler to mark the dowel at 12" locations. Label each mark with the numbers 1, 2, 3, 4, and 5. Wrap a rubber band tightly around the dowel at each number. These rubber bands will be used for attaching loads and the force meter. This is the rod for the Lab Lever.

Cut off the top. Cut a U–shaped channel in the side of the bottle at the top. Cut another U–shaped channel directly across from the first cut. Fill the bottle with dirt and rocks for stability. This is the fulcrum for the Lab Lever.

Test your Lab Lever by placing the rod in the channels at the top of the fulcrum at position #3. Ask a partner to put a hand over the fulcrum to keep the lever in place. Attach a load to position #1 while your partner holds the rod at position #3. The load may be tied onto the rod with string. Attach the force meter to position #5 by putting the clip under the rubber band at that position. Pull on the wood of the force meter and observe the amount of force needed to lift the load. This Lab Lever will be used in Labs in Lessons 12, 13, and 14. A partner will be needed for all the labs to hold the lever in place.

Investigative Loop – Using a Class One Lever – Lab 12–1

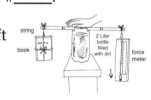
Lab 12–1

Focus Skills: predicting outcomes, drawing conclusions
Lab Materials: lab lever   force meter   load   bag
Paper Handouts: Lab Book   8.5" x 11" sheet of paper   Lab Record Cards
     a copy of Lab Graphic 12–1
Graphic Organizer: Make a Pocket Book and glue it side–by–side to the Lab Book. Glue Lab
     Graphics 12–1 to the left pocket.
Question: How does the placement of a fulcrum affect the amount of force needed to lift a load
     using a class one lever?
Research: Read *Lots of Science Library Book #12*. Review the question.
Prediction: Predict how different positions of the fulcrum will affect the amount of effort needed
     to lift the load: "I think it will take more effort to lift a load at position #_____."
Procedure: Place the fulcrum under Position #3 of the rod. Place the load on
     Position #1. Attach the force meter to Position #5 and pull down to lift
     the load. Move the fulcrum to Position #2 and follow the same
     procedure. Move the fulcrum to Position #4 and follow the same
     procedure.
Observations: Observe the force meter as each load is lifted.
Record the Data: Label three Lab Record Cards "Lab 12–1," and the date. Draw the three positions
     of the fulcrum, one on each card, and record the force meter number required to lift each
     load.
Conclusions: Compare the amount of force needed to lift the load in each position. Which
     position required more force? Which one required less force? Compare this to the
     prediction about the fulcrum.
Communicate the Conclusions: Label a Lab Record Card "Lab 12-1." Explain how the position of
     the fulcrum affected the amount of force needed to lift the load.
Spark Questions: Discuss questions sparked during the lab.
New Loop: Choose one question to investigate further.
     Design Your Own Experiment: Select a topic based upon this *Investigative Loop*
     experience. See page viii for more details.

Paper Handouts: Timeline Book a copy of Graphics 12C–D
Graphic Organizer: Glue Graphics 12C–D to the appropriate places in the Timeline Book. Copy the date of use on each picture. Draw a line from the graphic to the timeline and color the country where the tool was used. Add any other tools discovered in research to the Timeline Book.

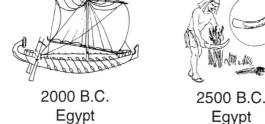

2000 B.C.
Egypt

2500 B.C.
Egypt

Experiences, Investigations, and Research

Select one or more of the following activities for individual or group enrichment projects. Allow your students to determine the format in which they would like to report, share, or graphically present what they have discovered. This should be a creative investigation that utilizes your students' strengths.

 1. Research and sketch the trebuchet, a medieval war machine. Explain its purposes and describe how it was used.

 2. Interview three people with different professions to determine what special tools they use. Speculate as to how these tools developed for each profession.

 3. Investigate the invention and use of a hand operated water pump. Describe it as a class one lever.

 4. Examine and sketch the following tools: oar, crowbar, weighing balance, scissors, and pliers. Identify and label the fulcrum, rod, effort, and load of each.

http://img.arc.
nasa.gov

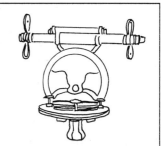

Technology – For centuries, the theodolite has been a surveyor's most important tool. Investigate how it works and its uses today. Add this tool to the *Tools in Time* Timeline Book.

Notes

What is a class two lever?

Tool Concepts:

- A class two lever always has a fulcrum on one end, and the force is applied on the other end. A load is placed between the two levers.
- The effort and the load move in the same direction, so force does not change in class two levers.
- Class two levers require less force to work when the effort arms are longer; however, the arm must move farther to do the work.
- All class two levers magnify force, but distance and speed are lessened.
- Simple machines that use the second class lever include nutcrackers, wheelbarrows, paper cutters, and bottle openers.

Vocabulary Words: class two lever   *composite

Read: *Lots of Science Library Book #13.*

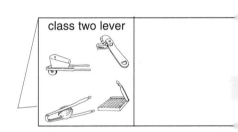

class two lever

Activities:

Class Two Levers – Graphic Organizer

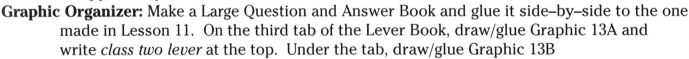

Focus Skills: describing forces, explaining forces
Paper Handouts: 8.5" x 11" sheet of paper
    Large Question and Answer Book made in Lesson 11
    a copy of Graphics 13A–B
Graphic Organizer: Make a Large Question and Answer Book and glue it side–by–side to the one made in Lesson 11. On the third tab of the Lever Book, draw/glue Graphic 13A and write *class two lever* at the top. Under the tab, draw/glue Graphic 13B

✎ Write/copy the names of the parts of the lever. Draw a black arrow showing where the force, or effort, is applied to this lever. This is called the input force. Draw a blue arrow showing where the force of the lever works, or the output force.

✎✎ Explain the class two lever and how force is applied to and outputted by this tool. Label the parts and list examples of the class two lever.

✎✎✎ Complete ✎✎. Explain how to change the amount of force needed to lift the load.

Investigative Loop – Using a Class Two Lever – Lab 13–1

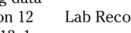

Focus Skills: comparing forces, comparing data
Paper Handouts: Lab Book made in Lesson 12   Lab Record Cards
    a copy of Lab Graphics 13–1
Lab Materials: force meter   lever used in Lab 12-1   load used in Lab 12-1

Graphic Organizer: Glue Lab Graphic 13–1 on the right pocket of the Lab Book.

Question: How does the placement of the load affect the force needed to lift it using a class two lever?

Research: Read *Lots of Science Library Book #13.* Review the question.

Predictions: Predict how different positions of the load will affect the force needed to lift the load: "I think the force will be greater with the load at Position #_____."

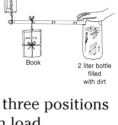
Lab 13–1

Procedure: Place the fulcrum on a table and place the rod on it at Position #5. Ask someone to hold the rod in place. Place the load on Position #2. Attach the force meter to Position #1 and lift the load. Move the load to Position #3 and follow the same procedure. Move the load to Position #4 and follow the same procedure.

Force Meter

Book

2 liter bottle filled with dirt

Observation: Observe the force meter as each load is lifted.

Record the Data: Label three Lab Record Cards "Lab 13–1," and the date. Draw the three positions of the load in the procedure, and record the force meter number to lift each load.

Conclusion: Place the three Lab Record Cards next to one another. Compare the force needed to lift the load in each position. Which position required more force? Which position required less? Make a statement about the placement of the load and the amount of force needed to lift a load. How does this compare to your prediction?

Communicate the Conclusions: Tell two people about this lab within the next 24 hours.

Spark Questions: Discuss questions sparked by the lab.

New Loop: Choose one question to investigate further.

✎✎✎ **Design Your Own Experiment:** Select a topic based upon this *Investigative Loop* experience. See page viii for more details.

Tools in Time – Timeline Book

Paper Handouts: Timeline Book
a copy of Graphics 13C–D

Graphic Organizer: Glue Graphics 13C–D to the appropriate places in the Timeline Book. Copy the date of use on the picture. Draw a line from the graphic to the timeline and color the region where the tool was used. Add any other tools discovered in research to the Timeline Book.

1220 A.D.
Northern Europe

2800 B.C.
China

xperiences, Investigations, and Research

Select one or more of the following activities for individual or group enrichment projects. Allow your students to determine the format in which they would like to report, share, or graphically present what they have discovered. This should be a creative investigation that utilizes your students' strengths.

1. Use a class two lever, such as a wheelbarrow to do work and explain how it makes work easier.

2. Explain a door as a class two lever.

Technology – Ancient people combined mud and other materials from nature to make bricks. This combination made a stronger building material. Make two little mounds to find out the importance of composite materials. Make one out of mud alone and one out of mud mixed with straw, grass, or cut-up branches. Write about this experience.

What is a class three lever?

Tool Concepts:

- A rake is a class three lever.
- The fulcrum of a class three lever is always at one end. In the case of a rake, the fulcrum is beside the wrist of its user.
- The force is applied to the middle of the rake, between the fulcrum and the load.
- The fan of the rake applies force on the leaves. This force is magnified in distance, not in strength.
- Class three levers include: rakes, fishing poles, tweezers, and a hammer hitting a nail.

Teacher's Note: An alternative assessment suggestion for this lesson is found on pages 72–73. If Graphics Pages are being consumed, first photocopy assessment graphics that are needed.

Vocabulary Words: class three lever   *elaborate   *efficient   *factory

Read: *Lots of Science Library Book #14.*

Activities:

Class Three Levers – Graphic Organizer

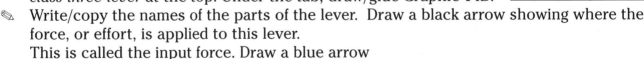

Focus Skills: comparing and contrast, labeling parts
Paper Handouts: Large Question and Answer Book used in Lesson 13
        a copy of Graphics 14A–B
Graphic Organizer: On the fourth tab, draw/glue Graphic 14A and write
        class three lever at the top. Under the tab, draw/glue Graphic 14B.

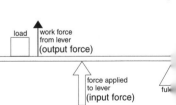

✎   Write/copy the names of the parts of the lever. Draw a black arrow showing where the force, or effort, is applied to this lever.
      This is called the input force. Draw a blue arrow
      showing where the force of the lever works, or the output force.

✎✎   Explain the class three lever and how force is applied to
      and outputted by this tool. Label the parts and list examples of
      the class three lever.

✎✎✎ Complete ✎✎. Explain how to change the amount of force
      needed to lift the load.

Investigative Loop – Using a Class Three Lever Lab 14–1

Focus Skills: recording and comparing data
Lab Materials: lever used in Lab 13-1   force meter   load used in Lab 13-1
Paper Handouts: 8.5" x 11" sheet of paper   Lab Book
        a copy of Lab Graphics 14–1   Lab Record Cards

Graphic Organizer: Make a Pocket Book and glue it side–by–side to the Lab Book. Glue Lab Graphic 14–1 on the left pocket of the Lab Book.

Question: How does the position of the effort affect the amount of force needed to lift a load in a class three lever?

Research: Read *Lots of Science Library Book #14*. Review the question.

Predictions: Predict how different positions of the effort will affect the force needed to lift the load: "I think the force will be greater with the effort at Position #_____."

Lab 14–1

Procedure: The fulcrum in this activity is the edge of a table. Place the rod under the fulcrum at Position #5. Place the load on Position #1. Attach the force meter to Position #2 and lift the load. Move the force meter to Position #3 and follow the same procedure. Move the force meter to Position #4 and follow the same procedure.

Observations: Observe the force meter as each load is lifted.

Record The Data: Label three Lab Record Cards "Lab 14–1," and the date. Draw the three positions of the effort and record the force meter number to lift each load.

Conclusions: Place the three Lab Record Cards next to one another. Compare the force needed to lift the load in each position. Which position required the most force? Which one required the least force? How does this compare to your prediction?

Communicate the Conclusions: Tell two people about your experiment in the next 24 hours.

Spark Questions: Discuss questions sparked by the lab.

New Loop: Choose one to investigate further.

✎✎✎ **Design Your Own Experiment:** Select a topic based upon this *Investigative Loop* experience. See page viii for more details.

All Classes of Levers

Focus Skill: comparing and contrasting data during oral discussion

Paper Handouts: Lab Book

Discussion Activity: Place the Lab Record Cards used in Lessons #12, #13, and #14 on the table. Compare the amount of force needed for the three classes of levers. Do you see any similarities among the levers? What differences do you see in their use of force? What types of jobs would each class of lever be best suited to perform?

Tools in Time – Timeline Book

Paper Handouts: Timeline Book   a copy of Graphics 14C–D

Graphic Organizer: Glue Graphics 14C–D to the appropriate places in the Timeline Book. Copy the date of use on the picture. Draw a line from the graphic to the timeline and color the region where the tool was used. Add any other tools discovered in research to the Timeline Book.

1450 A.D.
Germany

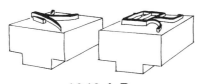

1040 A.D.
China

Experiences, Investigations, and Research

Select one or more of the following activities for individual or group enrichment projects. Allow your students to determine the format in which they would like to report, share, or graphically present what they have discovered. This should be a creative investigation that utilizes your students' strengths.

 1. Examine and sketch the following tools: tweezers, tongs, and a power shovel. Label each part of theses class three levers.

 2. Complete the invention you began in Lesson 6. Present it to a group.

 3. The human body has levers, can you find some of them? Hint: pick up an object.

http://www. pbs.org/wgbh/ amex/kids/ tech1900

Technology – Research the history of printing, from copying books by hand to the transferring of documents via e–mail. Include the introduction of multicolor printing and the process involved in four–color printing.

Technology – Investigate a form of modern communication and report on its invention, how it works, and its uses. Suggestions: fax machine, photocopier, e–mail, and the Internet.

Notes

What is a wheel and axle?

Tool Concepts:

- A wheel and axle is another example of a simple tool.
- Wheels are commonly used for transportation, but their greatest use is to reduce friction.
- When the wheel turns, the axle turns.
- When the axle turns, the wheel turns.
- A wheel and axle magnifies force. A small turning force applied to the wheel produces an increased force on the axle.
- Examples of a wheel and axle are the steering wheel of a car and a water wheel.

Vocabulary Words: wheel and axle   water wheel   *Industrial Revolution
*mass production

Read: *Lots of Science Library Book #15.*

Activities:

The Wheel and Axle – Graphic Organizer

Focus Skills: explaining forces, describing a tool
Paper Handouts: 8.5" x 11"sheet of paper   a copy of Graphics 15A–B
Graphic Organizer: Make a Large Question and Answer Book. Draw/glue
      Graphic 15A on the cover and write the name of the tool at the top.
      On the first tab, draw/glue Graphic 15B and write *The Tool.* Under the tab:
  ✎ Draw a wheel and axle. Draw black arrows to show how the wheel
      turns. Draw blue arrows to show how that affects the axle.
  ✎✎ Describe the wheel and axle. Explain how it uses force.
 ✎✎✎ Complete ✎✎. Research how this tool changed the world.

A Tool Sign

Focus Skill: application of information
Paper Handouts: The Tool Layered Look Book made in Lesson 4
      Make a list of wheels and axles that you see around you on the correct page.

Make a Wheel and Axle

Focus Skill: following directions
Paper Handout: thin cardboard   a copy of Graphics 15C–D   a pencil or a straw
      Read the directions aloud or ask your student to read them silently. As each direction is
      completed, check the box next to it. When the tool is completed, discuss the its parts
      and how it is used.

Focus Skills: quantitative observation, predicting outcome
Lab Materials: wheel and axle   pencil   ruler
Paper Handouts: Lab Book   Lab Record Cards   a copy of Graphics 15–1
Graphic Organizer: Draw/glue Lab Graphic 15–1 on the right pocket.
Question: How does a wheel and axle magnify force?
Research: Read the *Lots of Science Library Book #15* and review the question.
Predictions: Predict how the moving of the axle will affect the wheel. Think about the number of rotations the axle makes in comparison to the number of rotations the wheel makes at the same time. "If the axle rotates ___ times, the wheel will travel ....."
Procedure: Lay a ruler on the side of a table. Measure how far the wheel travels in one rotation. Measure how far the axle travels in one rotation, using the pencil only.
Observations: Observe the distance traveled in one rotation.
Record the Data: Label a Lab Record Card "Lab 15–1," and the date. Record the measurement of a rotation of the wheel. Label another Lab Record Card and record the same information about the axle.
Conclusions: Using the data collected on the Lab Record Cards, determine how far would the wheel would travel if the axle rotated 10 times? Make several similar calculations.
Communicate the Conclusions: Label another Lab Record, "Lab 15–1," and the date. Write a fact about your wheel and axle. "When the axle rotates__times, the wheel travels__ (distance)."
Spark Questions: Discuss questions sparked by the lab.
New Loop: Choose one question to investigate further.
  ✐✐✐ **Design Your Own Experiment:** Select a topic based upon this *Investigative Loop* experience. See page viii for more details.

Tools in Time – Timeline Book

Paper Handouts: Timeline Book   a copy of Graphics 15C–E
Graphic Organizer: Glue Graphics 15C–E to the appropriate places in the Timeline Book. Copy the date of use on the picture. Draw a line from the graphic to the timeline and color the country where the tool was used. Add any other tools discovered in research to the Timeline Book.

3200 B.C.
Iraq

2000 B.C.
India/Europe

1000 B.C.
Greece

Experiences, Investigations, and Research

Select one or more of the following activities for individual or group enrichment projects. Allow your students to determine the format in which they would like to report, share, or graphically present what they have discovered. This should be a creative investigation that utilizes your students' strengths.

 1. Disassemble a discarded wheeled toy. Investigate how it uses the wheel and axle.

 2. Compare and contrast ancient cultures that used the wheel and axle, such as Egyptians, with those that did not, such as the Aztecs.

Technology – Research the Industrial Revolution in Europe and America. Create a story about an imaginary family and show how the Industrial Revolution changed the life of each member in a short period of time.

Technology – List the pros and cons of early factories. Less expensive products are always appealing to consumers. Does this outweigh any negative effects on the culture? Present an argument for either or both sides and defend the arguments with researched facts.

Notes

How do we use the wheel and axle?

Tool Concepts:

- A screwdriver shows how a wheel and axle works. The handle is the wheel of the tool. It magnifies the turning force.
- The shaft of the screwdriver is the axle. The wheel turns the axle.
- The turning of the wheel is the input force.
- The force that turns the screw is the output force.
- This tool increases force, while decreasing speed and distance.
- Other simple machines that use the wheel and axle in this way are the round doorknob and the steering wheel of a car.
- A water wheel also demonstrates how a wheel and axle works. It produces more force at the axle, which increases speed and distance.

Teacher's Note: An alternative assessment suggestion for this lesson is found on pages 72–73. If Graphic Pages are being consumed, first photocopy assessment graphics that are needed.

Vocabulary Words: shaft   input force   output force   *accuracy

Read: *Lots of Science Library Book #16.*

Activities:

The Wheel and Axle – Graphic Organizer

Focus Skill: applying information
Paper Handouts: Large Question and Answer Book from Lesson 15
    a copy of Graphics 16A
Graphic Organizer: Using the Book from Lesson 15, draw/glue
    Graphic 16A on the second tab and write *The Tool at Work.*
    Under the tab:

- ✎ Write/copy the examples of the wheel and axle: *screwdriver, doorknob, water wheel.*
- ✎✎ Explain how the wheel and axle is used in these tools.
- ✎✎✎ Complete ✎✎. Explain the input and output forces of the wheel and axle.

Paper Handouts: Timeline Book   a copy of Graphics 16B–C
Graphic Organizer: Glue Graphics 16B–C to the appropriate
places in the Timeline Book. Copy the date of use on
each picture. Draw a line from the graphic to the timeline
and color the country where the tool was used. Add any
other tools discovered in research to the Timeline Book.

900 B.C.
Assyria

900 A.D.
Europe

xperiences, Investigations, and Research

Select one or more of the following activities for individual or group enrichment projects. Allow
your students to determine the format in which they would like to report, share, or graphically
present what they have discovered. This should be a creative investigation that utilizes your
students' strengths.

1. Use a screwdriver and talk about the forces being used with this wheel and axle tool.

2. Disassemble a discarded doorknob. Describe a doorknob as a wheel and axle.

3. Describe each of the following as a wheel and axle:
   a) key turned in a keyhole b) water faucet turning water off and on
   c) handle of a pencil sharpener.

4. Investigate and sketch a windlass, one of the first uses of a wheel and axle. Explain its
ability to move heavy objects.

5. Explain how a windmill converts the kinetic energy of moving wind into mechanical
energy. Do the same for a turbine with steam and a water wheel with water. Compare
and contrast these three inventions.

6. Write a paper defending the following statement: *The water wheel was the greatest
and most stable source of power before the use of steam.*

7. Read and discuss *Choo Choo* by Virginia Lee Burton ✎.

8. Read and discuss *Charles Lindberg: Hero Pilot* by David R. Collins ✎✎ ✎✎✎.

Technology – The idea of products being disposable was an unknown concept in 1903
when King C. Gillette first produced a razor made to be thrown away when the blade
became dull. Then in 1949, Baron Marcel Bich founded a small pen company. He dropped
the "h" to create his trademark name, Bic™. In 1953, he marketed his famous throw
away Bic™ pen. Today we are very familiar with disposable items. Investigate disposable
items and the impact they have had on the world.

What is a fixed pulley?

Tool Concepts:

- A pulley is simple tool. It is a wheel with a rope that runs along the groove of the wheel.
- A load is attached to one end of the rope. The other end is pulled to move the load.
- A fixed pulley is attached to a structure. A single fixed pulley changes the direction of the input force rather than magnifying it.
- Fixed pulleys change the direction of input force. This is the same thing that happens with a class one lever. Instead of using a rod, force is applied to the rope. The center of the wheel acts like a fulcrum.
- The weight of the object being lifted is called the load and the distance it rises is called the load distance.
- Force exerted on the rope is the effort and the distance the rope is moved down is the effort distance.
- A fixed pulley can have more than one wheel in the system.
- Fixed pulleys are used in raising curtains, blinds, and sails.

Teacher's Note: Investigative Loops for Lessons 17, 18, and 19 use pulleys. You will need a crossba to attach the pulleys to for the labs. Use the pulleys made in this lesson if the load that your force meter is calibrated for is light enough to be lifted by them. If your force meter needs a heavier load you may purchase two 1" metal pulleys at most hardware stores. The load can be a book tied to th pulley strings or flour in a plastic secured bag attached with a paper clip. Before each lab, check t force needed to lift the load so that can be compared to the force needed to lift it with the pulley systems.

Vocabulary Words: pulley   wheel   rope   load distance   effort distance
fixed pulley

Read: *Lots of Science Library Book #17.*

Activities:

The Fixed Pulley – Graphic Organizer

Focus Skills: labeling parts, describing a tool
Paper Handouts: 8.5" x 11" sheet of paper   a copy of Graphics 17A–B
Graphic Organizer: Make a Hot Dog, 3 Tab Book. On the first tab, draw/glue Graphic 17A and write *fixed pulley* at the top. Under the tab, draw/glue graphic 17B and label the parts of the tool.

   ✎   Draw a black arrow showing the direction of the effort on this pulley. Draw a blue arrow showing the direction the load moves with that effort.

   ✎✎   Describe the fixed pulley, its parts, and its uses.

   ✎✎✎   Complete ✎✎. Explain the load distance and the effort distance on this pulley.

A Tool Sign

Focus Skill: application of information
Paper Handout: The Tool Layered Look Book made in Lesson 4
On the page titled *pulley,* list the pulleys that you see around you.

TOOLS	
make work easier	
inclined plane	wedge
screw	lever
wheel and axle	pulley

Make a Pulley

Focus Skill: following directions
Paper Handout: thin cardboard   a copy of Graphics 17C–E   1 yard of string
a tack or tape
Read the directions aloud or ask your students to read them silently. As each direction is completed, check the box next to it. When the tool is completed, discuss the parts and its uses.

Investigative Loop – Experience the Fixed Pulley – Lab 17–1

Focus Skill: evaluating the force of a tool
Lab Materials: pulley made in previous activity or 1" metal pulley
load   force meter
Paper Handouts: two sheets of 8.5" x 11" paper
a copy of Graphic 17F   Lab Record Cards
a copy of Lab Graphic 17–1   Lab Book

Lab 17–1

Graphic Organizer: Make a Pocket Book and glue it side–by–side to the Lab Book. Glue Lab Graphic 17–1 on the left pocket of the Lab Book.
Question: How does a fixed pulley magnify force?
Research: Read *Lots of Science Library Book #17* and review the Question.
Predictions: Predict how the fixed pulley will magnify the force needed to lift the load. "It will take ___ amount of force to lift the load with this pulley."
Procedure: Set up the fixed pulley and attach the load to it. Lift the load with the pulley by attaching the force meter to the effort end and pulling the load up.

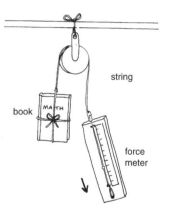

string

book

force meter

Observation: Observe the force meter when the load is lifted.
Record the Data: Label a Lab Record Card "Lab 17–1," and the date. Draw the load being lifted with the force meter and record data for the load lifted by the fixed pulley.
Conclusions: Use the data collected to evaluate the force of this tool. How much force was saved or wasted by using the pulley? On the Lab Record Card, write a true statement about the use of fixed pulleys when lifting a load. "A fixed pulley is …."
Communicate the Conclusions: Be a reporter for a tool magazine. Make a Half Book, turn it so the fold is on the left side, and glue Graphic 17F on the front. Begin a report on the effectiveness of pulleys. Write an introductory paragraph on pulleys and at least one paragraph on the fixed pulley. This Half Book Magazine Article will be used in Lessons 18–19.
Spark Questions: Discuss questions sparked by this lab.
New Loop: Choose one question to investigate further.
✎✎✎ **Design Your Own Experiment:** Select a topic based upon this *Investigative Loop* experience. See page viii for more details.

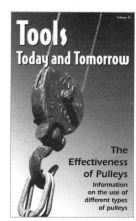

Tools
Today and Tomorrow

The **Effectiveness of Pulleys**
Information on the use of different types of pulleys

Paper Handouts: Timeline Book   a copy of Graphics 17G–I
Graphic Organizer: Glue Graphics 17G–I to the appropriate places in the Timeline Book. Copy the date of use on the picture. Draw a line from the graphic to the timeline and color the region where the tool was used. Add any other tools discovered in research to the Timeline Book.

1100 A.D.
Europe

1250 B.C.
Greece

10 B.C.
Rome

http://www.
nationalgeographic.
com/features/96/
inventions/index.
html

Technology – In early years, the power for tools came from the worker or from animals. The creation of engines began a new era in technology. Research the steam engine and find out about its invention, how it creates power, and its early uses.

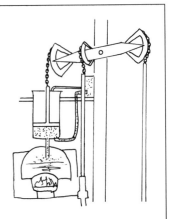

Notes

What is a moveable pulley?

Tool Concepts:

- In a moveable pulley, the wheel of the pulley is attached to the load. The wheel moves up and down with the load.
- The direction of the force does not change.
- Force is magnified with the moveable pulley; however, distance and speed are decreased.
- When using a movable pulley, a load travels half the distance of the effort. For every foot you want the load to lift, you must pull the rope two feet.
- The force needed to lift a load equals half the weight of a load. Moveable pulleys are often used in large construction cranes.

Vocabulary Words: moveable pulley   *internal combustion engine   *jet engine

Read: *Lots of Science Library Book #18.*

Activities:

The Moveable Pulley – Graphic Organizer

Focus Skills: describing forces, explaining a tool
Paper Handouts: The 3 Tab Book made in Lesson 17   a copy of Graphics 18A–B
Graphic Organizer: On the 3 Tab Book, draw/glue Graphic 18A on the middle tab and write *moveable pulley* at the top. Under the tab, draw/glue Graphic 18B and label the parts of the tool.

- ✎ Draw a black arrow showing the direction of the effort on this pulley. Draw a blue arrow showing the direction the load moves with that effort.
- ✎✎ Describe the moveable pulley, its parts, and its use of forces.
- ✎✎✎ Complete ✎✎. Explain the load distance and the effort distance of this pulley.

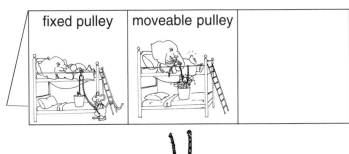

Investigative Loop – Experience the Moveable Pulley – Lab 18–1

Lab 18–1

Focus Skills: evaluating the force of a tool, predicting an outcome

Lab Materials: pulley made in Lesson 17   10–16 ounce substance used in Lab 17–1
force meter

Paper Handouts: Lab Pocket Book   Lab Record Cards
a copy of Lab Graphic 18–1
Half Book Magazine Article from Lesson 17

Graphic Organizer: Glue Lab Graphic 18–1 on the right pocket of the
Lab Book.

Question: How does a moveable pulley magnify force?

Research: Read *Lots of Science Library Book #18* and review the Question.

Predictions: Predict how a moveable pulley will magnify the force
needed to lift the load. "It will take ___ amount of force to lift the load
with this pulley."

Procedure: Set up the moveable pulley and attach the load to it. Lift the load with the pulley by
attaching the force meter to the effort end and pulling the load up.

Observations: Observe the force meter as the load is lifted each time.

Record the Data: Label a Lab Record Card "Lab 18–1," and the date. Sketch the lab and record the
force meter number for each lift of the load.

Conclusions: Use the Lab Record Card data to evaluate the force of this tool. How much force was
saved or wasted by using the pulley?

Communicate the Conclusions: Write a true statement about the use of moveable pulleys when
lifting a load on a Lab Record Card. "A moveable pulley is ...." Put the Lab Record Card
in the correct pocket. Continue the Half Book Magazine Article on the effectiveness of
pulleys. Information on the moveable pulley should be a separate paragraph in this article.

Spark Questions: Discuss questions sparked by this lab.

New Loop: Choose one question to investigate further.

✎✎✎ **Design Your Own Experiment:** Select a topic based upon this *Investigative Loop*
experience. See page viii for more details.

Tools in Time – Timeline Book

Paper Handouts: Timeline Book   a copy of Graphics 18C–D

Graphic Organizer: Glue Graphics 18C–D on the appropriate places in the Timeline
Book. Copy the date of use on the picture. Draw a line from the graphic to
the timeline and color the region where the tool was used. Add any other
tools discovered in research to the Timeline Book.

400 B.C.
Italy

1200 A.D.
Europe/India

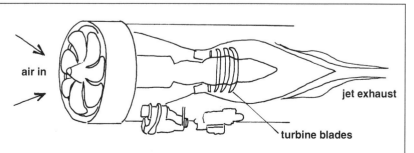

Technology – Create a timeline for
engines. Include the major uses of
the engines at the time of their
invention and explain how their
uses changed through the years.

air in

jet exhaust

turbine blades

What is a compound pulley?

Tool Concepts:

- A compound pulley is made from one fixed pulley and one moveable pulley. This combinatio magnifies force and changes the direction of the force.
- Another name for the compound pulley is a block and tackle.
- A block and tackle can be found in auto repair shops where heavy auto parts need to be lifte and is also used for the raising and lowering scaffolding at construction sites.
- With a compound pulley, the load travels half the distance of the effort. For every foot you want the load to lift, you must pull the rope two feet.

Teacher's Note: An alternative assessment suggestion for this lesson is found on pages 72–73. If Graphic Pages are being consumed, first photocopy assessment graphics that are needed .

Vocabulary Words: compound pulley   force load   magnifies   *artisan
*electric power

Read: *Lots of Science Library Book #19.*

Activities:

The Compound Pulley – Graphic Organizer

Focus Skills: describing a tool, explaining forces
Paper Handouts: 3 Tab Book used in Lesson 18   a copy of Graphics 19A–B
Graphic Organizer: On the third tab, draw/glue Graphic 19A. Write *compound pulley* at the top o the tab.   Under the tab, draw/glue Graphic 19B and label the parts of the tool.

- ✎ Draw a black arrow showing the direction of the effort on this pulley. Draw a blue arrow showing the direction the load moves with that effort.
- ✎✎ Describe the compound pulley, its parts, and uses.
- ✎✎✎ Complete ✎✎. Describe the load distance and the effort distance on this pulley.

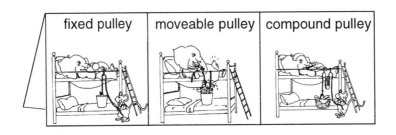

Investigative Loop – Experience the Compound Pulley Lab 19–1

Focus Skills: evaluating the force of a tool, recording data

Lab Materials: pulley made in Lesson 17   load used in Lab 18–1
   force meter

Paper Handouts: 8.5" x 11" sheet of paper   Lab Book
   Lab Record Cards   a copy of Lab Graphic 19–1

Graphic Organizer: Make a Pocket Book and glue it side–by–side to the
   Lab Book. Glue Lab Graphic 19–1 on the left pocket.

Question: How does a compound pulley magnify force?

Research: Read *Lots of Science Library Book #19* and review the
   Question.

Predictions: Predict how a compound pulley will magnify the force
   needed to lift the load. "A compound pulley will take ___
   amount of force to lift the load with this pulley."

Procedure: Set up the compound pulley and attach the load to it. Lift the load with the pulley by
   attaching the force meter to the effort end and pulling the load up.

Observations: Observe the force meter as the load is lifted.

Record the Data: Label a Lab Record Card "Lab 19–1," and the date. Sketch the lab, and record the
   force meter number for each lift of the load.

Conclusions: How much force was saved or wasted by using the pulley?

Communicate the Conclusions: On a Lab Record Card write a true statement about the use of
   compound pulleys when lifting a load: "A compound pulley is ...." Put the Lab Record
   Card in the correct pocket. Write a paragraph about the compound pulley in your
   magazine article.

Spark Questions: Discuss questions sparked by this lab.

New Loop: Choose one question to investigate further.

   ✎✎✎ **Design Your Own Experiment:** Select a topic based upon this *Investigative Loop*
   experience. See page viii for more details.

The Effectiveness of Pulleys

Focus Skill: comparing and contrasting

Paper Handouts: Lab Book   Half Book Magazine Article

Graphic Organizer: Using the Lab Record Cards from the pulley experiments,
   compare the results of each experiment. Which pulley magnified forces the
   most? Which one magnified forces the least? Were any of the results the
   same in these experiments? How did they differ? Finish writing your
   magazine article and include the data you discover in these comparisons.

Tools in Time – Timeline Book

Paper Handouts: Timeline Book   a copy of Graphics 19C–E

Graphic Organizer: Glue Graphics 19C–E to the appropriate places in the Timeline Book. Copy the
   date of use on the picture. Draw a line from the
   graphic to the timeline and color the region
   where the tool was used. Add any other tools
   discovered in research to the Timeline Book.

1500 B.C.
Middle East

500 B.C.
Greece

100 A.D.
Egypt

Experiences, Investigations, and Research

Select one or more of the following activities for individual or group enrichment projects. Allow your students to determine the format in which they would like to report, share, or graphically present what they have discovered. This should be a creative investigation that utilizes your students' strengths.

 1. Visit a working construction site and observe a crane. Find the pulleys used in the crane. Are all the three classes of levers used in a crane?

 2. Read and discuss *Mike Mulligan and His Steam Shovel* by Virginia Lee Burton.

Technology – Thomas Edison, in the United States, and Joseph Swan, in Britain, invented the light bulb in the same year. Investigate how it was made, what it was used for, and how it changed life in the countries where it was introduced.

Technology – Investigate the importance of modern sewage systems. Research past and present cholera epidemics and explain methods of prevention.

Notes

Great Science Adventures

What are the six simple tools?

Tool Concepts:

- Review of the previous lessons on work and the six simple tools.
- When two or more tools are used in one instrument, it is called a complex machine.

Read: *Lots of Science Library Book #20.*

Teachers' Note: There are two types of holders your students can make to store the 3D Graphic Organizers created in this program. The *Tool Box* is a paper box about 18" x 6" x 6" with a hand and six compartments that hold the books. The *Tool Box Book* is a multipage book with a "tool box" cover.

Activities:

Tool Box

Focus Skill: sorting tools
Paper Handouts: 6 sheets of 12" x 18" construction paper
        Graphic Organizers from previous lessons
Graphic Organizer: Follow the directions below to make a Tool Box. When completed, place the
        Graphic Organizers for each tool in a separate compartment.

1. Using 6 sheets of 12" x 18" paper, make a Taco Fold on each one. Cut off the rectangle to form a square.
2. Fold the square into a Shutter Fold. Unfold and fold into another Shutter Fold, perpendicular to the previous one.
3. Cut along two fold lines on opposite sides of the large square.
4. Collapse in and glue the cut tabs to form an open box. Complete all sheets of paper in this manner.
5. Use a sheet of a different color of paper to cut two 1" x 11" strips to be the handles of the tool box.
6. Glue three display boxes together, inserting both ends of one handle about 1" deep between the sides being glued, toward the inner edge of the box. Repeat this with the other three boxes.
7. Use three 5" strips of wide tape to tape the two sets of boxes together. The tape will form a hinge on the tool box.
8. Close the tool box and tape along the outside of the hinge for added strength.

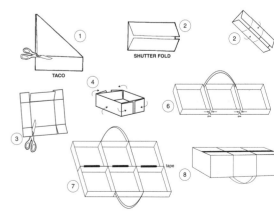

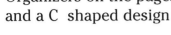
Focus Skills: sorting tools and organizing material
Paper Handouts: 3 sheets of 12" x 18" construction paper
   Graphic Organizers from previous lessons
Graphic Organizer: Fold each paper into an off-centered
   Shutter Fold as shown in the illustration.
   Glue the pages in the left fold, as you would a Layered Look Book. Arrange all the Graphic
   Organizers on the pages and glue them in place. If desired, use paper for an oval "latch"
   and a C shaped design for a handle to the Tool Box Book.

Tools in Time – Timeline Book

Paper Handouts: Timeline Book   a copy of Graphic 20A
Graphic Organizer: Glue Graphic 20A to the appropriate place in the Timeline Book. Copy the
   date of use on the picture. Draw a line from the graphic to the timeline and color the
   region where the tool was used. Add any other tools discovered in research to the
   Timeline Book.

Experiences, Investigations, and Research

1230 B.C.
Egypt

Select one or more of the following activities for individual or group
enrichment projects. Allow your students to determine the format in
which they would like to report, share, or graphically present what they
have discovered. This should be a creative investigation that utilizes your
students' strengths.

 1. Display various household tools. Ask your students which simple tools are found in
   each.

 2. List examples of machines that make work easier by increasing forces. List examples of
   machines that make work easier by increasing the distance over which a force is
   applied. List examples of machines that make work easier by changing the direction of
   the force being used.

 3. Explain these two types of work: the input work a person does on a machine and the
   resulting output work done by the machine.

 4. Explain this statement: *The efficiency of a machine equals the ratio between the amount of
   energy produced, or the output energy, and the amount of energy expended, or the input
   energy. Since the efficiency is expressed as a percentage, it is always less than 100%.*

 5. Define compound machines and look for them in your world. Sketch an example of a
   compound machine and list the simple machines used in its construction.

Technology – Research the car. Investigate how it is made
today, the use of robots in its production, the materials used
to make a car, and the number of cars produced annually.
Predict future modes of transportation.

Great Science Adventures

What are gears?

Tool Concepts:

- Gears are wheels with teeth along the outer edge.
- The teeth of the gears are called cogs.
- When one gear, called the drive wheel, turns, it causes the gear next to it to turn.
- Drive wheels can make smaller wheels turn faster, or make larger wheels turn slower.
- Spur gears lie next to each other, magnify force, and reverse direction.
- Rack and pinion gears have one wheel and a rack with teeth. They move back and forth instead of around.
- Bevel gears come together at an angle, changing force and direction.
- Worm gears have a wheel on a screw thread to change the force and the direction.

Vocabulary Words: gears   cog   spur gear   rack and pinion   bevel gears
worm gears   *microchips

Read: *Lots of Science Library Book #21.*

Activities:

Types of Gears – Graphic Organizer

Focus Skills: cause and effect, explaining forces
Paper Handouts: 8.5" x 11" sheet of paper   a copy of Graphics 21A–E
Graphic Organizer: Make a 4 Door Book. Draw/glue Graphic 21A on the cover and write the name of the tool. Open the book and draw/glue one type of gear on each tab using Graphics 21B–E. Under each tab:

✎ Draw the gear. Draw black arrows showing how the drive gear turns. Draw blue arrows showing the effect of that on the other parts of the gear.

✎✎ Describe each gear. Explain how the movement of the drive gear affects the movement of the other parts of the gear system.

✎✎✎ Complete ✎✎. Investigate examples of uses for each type of gear.

Gears

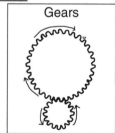

spur gears

rack and pinion gea

bevel gears

worm gea

Make Gears

Focus Skill: following directions

Paper Handouts: a copy of Graphic 21F   poster board

Read the directions aloud or ask your students to read them silently. As each direction is completed, check the box next to it. When the tool is completed, discuss the parts and its uses. Put a drinking glass inside the large gear for support and insert the cogs of the small gear into the cogs of the large one. Discover how many times the small gear turns in one rotation of the large gear.

Tools in Time – Timeline Book

Paper Handouts: Timeline Book   a copy of Graphics 21G–I

Graphic Organizer: Glue Graphics 21G–I to the appropriate places in the Timeline Book. Copy the date on each picture. Draw a line from the graphic to the timeline and color the region where the tool was used. Add any other tools discovered in research to the Timeline Book.

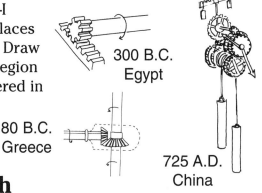

300 B.C.
Egypt

80 B.C.
Greece

725 A.D.
China

Experiences, Investigations, and Research

Select one or more of the following activities for individual or group enrichment projects. Allow your students to determine the format in which they would like to report, share, or graphically present what they have discovered. This should be a creative investigation that utilizes your students' strengths.

 1. Disassemble discarded clock and investigate its gears.

2. Gears are produced in a wide range of sizes, from tiny watch gears to huge gears that turn the propellers on supertankers. Research gears and report how they are used in various types of equipment.

3. The ratio of the gears determines the speed at which the gears rotate and the amount of force they transmit. Ratio is determined by comparing the number of cogs on the smaller gear with the number of cogs on the larger one. If the smaller gear has 20 cogs and the larger gear has 60 cogs, the ratio is 1 to 3. Draw and label gears with the following ratios: 1 to 2, 1 to 5, and 3 to 7.

Technology – Interview someone who used computers 20 to 30 years ago. Find out what you can about these first computers: how big they were, how they operated, and what could be accomplished with them.

Technology – If you have a computer, list all the jobs your family uses it to do. How were those jobs accomplished before the computer?

Great Science Adventures

What are cams and cranks?

Tool Concepts:

- A cam is a wheel and axle with an extension attached to the wheel.
- A cam operates valves in a car engine cylinder.
- A crank is a wheel with a rod attached to it. The other end of the rod is hinged so that the r[od] moves backward and forward as the wheel turns.
- A crankshaft is used to create rotating movement in a car engine.
- A crank drives the needle of a sewing machine up and down, and two trains of cams and cranks move feed–dogs that move the fabric.

Vocabulary Words: cam   crank   hinged   crankshaft   *diagnostic

Read: *Lots of Science Library Book #22.*

Activities:

Cams and Cranks – Graphic Organizer

Focus Skills: explaining a process, describing tools
Paper Handouts: 8.5" x 11" sheet of paper   a copy of Graphics 22A–E
Graphic Organizer: Make a 4 Door Book. Draw/glue Graphic 22A on the cover and write/copy the title, *Cams and Cranks*. Draw/glue Graphics 22B–E on each tab. Under the tab:

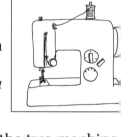
Cams and Crank[s]

✏ Write/dictate clue words: *cam – wheel with a bump; crank – wheel with a rod, rod on hinge; sewing machine – uses cams and cranks; car engine – uses cams and cranks.*

✏✏ Explain how cams and cranks use force to work. Describe their uses in the two machine[s].

✏✏✏ Complete ✏✏. Explain how the forces are changed in each tool. Research each machine and include new information in your explanations.

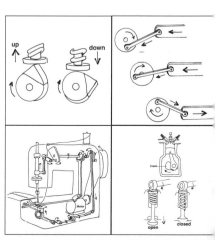

Paper Handouts: Timeline Book   a copy of Graphics 22F–G
Graphic Organizer: Glue Graphics 22F–G to the appropriate places in the
Timeline Book. Copy the date of use on each picture. Draw a line
from the graphic to the timeline and color the region where the tool
was used. Add any other tools discovered in research to the
Timeline Book.

700 B.C.
Persia

1400 A.D.
Europe

xperiences, Investigations, and Research

Select one or more of the following activities for individual or group enrichment projects. Allow
your students to determine the format in which they would like to report, share, or graphically
present what they have discovered. This should be a creative investigation that utilizes your
students' strengths.

1. Watch a sewing machine work. Open the side of the machine to see the parts move as it
    sews. If possible, take off the top and bottom plates of the machine and observe the
    parts of the machine.

2. Ask a car mechanic questions about the engine of a car. Discover all you can about
    cams, cranks, and the crankshaft.

3. Research the winch. Explain how it is a crank. Give example of its use, past and
    present.

http://www.
usfirst.org

Technology – With recent new discoveries about DNA,
discussions about genetic engineering are increasing.
Investigate this procedure. Interview several people to find
out what they think about genetic engineering. Discover
the facts, consider the opinions of others, and then form
your own opinion. Be able to defend your position.

What is a spring?

Tool Concepts:

- Springs play an important job in many common machines.
- Springs have three main uses in machines. One is to return something to its previous positio[n]
- Second, springs are used in weighing machines.
- Third, springs can be used to store energy.
- A stapler uses a spring to push and hold staples in place.
- Heavy springs between the wheel and axle and the body of a car absorb shock waves.
- A vehicle's torsion bar, or antiroll bar, acts as a spring.

Teacher's Note: An alternative assessment suggestion for this lesson is found on pages 72–73. If Graphic Pages are being consumed, first photocopy assessment graphics that are needed.

Vocabulary Words: spring   position   energy   stapler   absorb   *torsion bar

Read: *Lots of Science Library Book #23.*

Activities:

How We Use Springs – Graphic Organizer

Focus Skills: describing the use of a tool, explaining forces
Paper Handouts: 8.5" x 11" sheet of paper   a copy of Graphics 23A–E
Graphic Organizer: Make a 4 Door Book. Glue Graphics 23A on the cover and title it *Springs*. Draw/glue Graphics 23B–E on each tab.

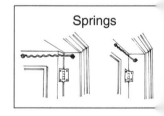
Springs

✎ Write/dictate clue words under each tab: *spring returns to position; springs weigh loads; springs store energy; stapler, car springs.*

✎✎ Describe how the spring works in each tool.

✎✎✎ Complete ✎✎. Research other examples of the use of springs in tools and include the information in your descriptions.

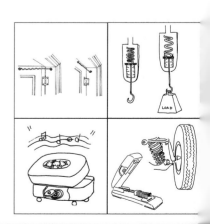

Paper Handouts: Timeline Book   a copy of Graphics 23F–G

Graphic Organizer: Glue Graphics 23F–G to the appropriate places in the Timeline Book. Copy the date of use on the picture. Draw a line from the graphic to the timeline and color the region where the tool was used. Add any other tools discovered in research to the Timeline Book.

1902 A.D.
Great Britain

600 A.D.
Rome

Experiences, Investigations, and Research

Select one or more of the following activities for individual or group enrichment projects. Allow your students to determine the format in which they would like to report, share, or graphically present what they have discovered. This should be a creative investigation that utilizes your students' strengths.

1. Look for springs around you. Make a list of the springs you find and the jobs that they do.

2. Investigate the process of annealing wire for use in a coil spring. Explain its importance in the effectiveness of a spring.

3. Alloys are added to metals that are used to make springs. Find out which metals are added and why.

4. On the back of the Tool Layered Look Book, list the cams, cranks, springs, and gears that you see around you.

TOOLS

make work easier

inclined plane	wedge
screw	lever
wheel and axle	pulley

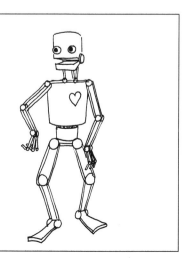

Technology – Predict the future of technology. Explain the changes you think will take place, and why. Write a futuristic story about life 50 years from today.

Technology – Read a futuristic science fiction book or story, or watch a movie about one. Critique the story using information you have learned about technology. Write your own science fiction story about the future.

How are tools powered?

Tool Concepts:

- Simple tools are useful to people because they make our work easier.
- Simple tools can be powered by one person.
- Tools became easier to use when the power of an animal was added.
- The world of tools and technology changed dramatically with the invention of engines.
- Plows have changed little over thousands of years, except in the way that they are powered.

Vocabulary Words: technology   power   simple tools   complex machines

steam engine   gasoline engine   diesel engine

Read: *Lots of Science Library Book #24.*

Activities:

Powering a Tool – Graphic Organizer

Focus Skills: sequencing, describing tools
Paper Handouts: 4 sheets of 8.5" x 11" paper or a 12" x 18" sheet of construction paper
    a copy of Graphics 24A–D   index cards
Graphic Organizer: Make 4 Pyramid Projects using the 8.5" x 11" paper. Glue them into four
    dioramas. Draw/glue one graphic in each Pyramid Project. Alternatively make a 4 Door
    Book with the 12" x 18" paper. Glue a graphic on each tab. Write about each picture on the
    index cards for the diorama or under the tab in the 4 Door Book about each picture.
    ✎ Write/dictate words about the pictures: *farmer pushes plow, plow is pulled by animal, plow
    uses wheel, plow is engine powered.*
    ✎✎ Describe how each plow is powered and the effect it might have on the worker.
    ✎✎✎ Complete ✎✎. Describe the amount of effort used by the farmer in each picture and how
    the introduction of engines impacted farming.

Tools in Time – Timeline Book

Paper Handouts: Timeline Book   a copy of Graphics 24E–G
Graphic Organizer: Glue Graphics 24E–G to the appropriate places
    in the Timeline Book. Copy the date of use on the picture.
    Draw a line from the graphic to the timeline and color the
    region where the tool was used. Add any other tools
    discovered in research to the Timeline Book.

1939 A.D.
USA/USSR

1963 A.D.
Holland

1940 A.D.
Papua New Guin

Experiences, Investigations, and Research

Select one or more of the following activities for individual or group enrichment projects. Allow your students to determine the format in which they would like to report, share, or graphically present what they have discovered. This should be a creative investigation that utilizes your students' strengths.

 1. Visit a working farm and watch a modern plow in action. Compare and contrast a plow to a garden tiller.

 2. Plow, till, or hoe a garden plot and plant a garden.

 3. Compare and contrast the use of engine powered machines and the use of animal powered machines to do work. For example, animals get sick and machines do not, but machines can break.

 4. Using all, or some, of the activities created in this program, make a cumulative project. Use *The Big Book of Books and Activities* by Dinah Zike for display ideas. Visit www.dinah.com or call 1–210–698–0123 for a catalog.

http://www.apase.bc.ca/unmixed/una9.html

Technology – What do you think it was like for the people of Papua New Guinea to see a helicopter fly in the air and then land near their homes? Write about the impact of living in the Stone Age and suddenly experiencing the Modern Age through one event. Find out about this country and what has happened there over recent decades.

Notes

Great Science Adventures

Additional *Tools in Time* Entries
Optional

50	Europe	Muzzle–loading gun
00	Germany	Pocket watch
38	Spain	Diving bell
50	Spain	Musket
55	Switzerland	Pencil
00	Holland	Microscope
04	France	Hand grenade
08	Holland	Telescope
20	England	Submarine
37	France	Umbrella
43	Italy	Barometer
68	England	Reflecting telescope
75	Holland	Spring–driven clock
09	Italy	Piano
18	England	Machine gun
34	Germany	Fire extinguisher
45	Sweden	Mass production of wrought iron
83	France	Steamboat
83	France	Hot air balloon
86	Scotland	Threshing machine
02	USA	Cotton gin
03	England	Steam train
22	France	Photograph
30	France	Sewing machine
39	Scotland	Bicycle
60	Belgium	Gasoline engine
74	USA	Typewriter
76	USA	Telephone
85	Germany	Motorcycle
92	USA	Gasoline–powered tractor
04	USA	Escalator
03	USA	Airplane flight
08	USA	Model T automobile

1922	Germany	Motion picture
1925	Scotland	Television
1930	England	Jet engine
1942	France	Aqualung
1942	Germany	Launch of rocket
1948	England	Computer with vacuum tubes
1950	USA	Color television broadcasting
1954	USSR	Nuclear power station
1955	England	Hovercraft
1957	USSR	Launch of satellite
1959	USA	Transistor used in computers
1960	USA	Laser
1961	USSR	Manned space flight
1963	England	Home video recorder
1966	USA/USSR	Unmanned space probe on moon
1969	USA	Manned US *Apollo* spacecraft lands on moon
1970	USA	Floppy disks for computers
1971	USSR	Space station
1981	USA	Space shuttle
1981	USA	Personal computer, hard disk storage
1988	USA	Parallel processing in computers
1988	Japan	Longest suspension bridge
1990	USA	Hubble space telescope in orbit

Great Science Adventures

Assessment: An Ongoing Process

Students do not have to memorize every vocabulary word or fact presented in these lessons. It more important to teach them general science processes and cause–and–effect relationships. Factual content is needed for students to understand processes, but it should become familiar t them through repeated exposure, discussion, reading, research, presentations, and a small amou of memorization. You can determine the amount of content your students have retained by aski specific questions that begin with the following words: *name, list, define, label, identify, draw, an outline.*

Try to determine through discussion how much content your students have retained. Determine how many general ideas, concepts, and processes your students understand by asking them to describe or explain them. Ask leading questions that require answers based upon thought and analysis, not just facts. Use the following words and phrases as you discuss and evaluate: *why, how, describe, explain, determine,* and *predict.* Questions may sound like this:

What would happen if _____?   *Compare _____ to _____.*
Why do you think _____ happens?   *What does ___have in common with __?*
What do you think about _____?   *What is the importance of _____?*

Alternative Assessment Strategies

If you need to know specifically what your students have retained or need to assign your students a grade for the content learned in this program, we suggest using one of the following assessment strategies.

By the time your students have completed a lesson in this program, they will have observed, discussed, and written about the concepts of the lesson. However, it is still important for you to let the students know the concepts that you will be assessing prior to the assessment. By makin your students aware of what you expect them to know, you provide a structure for their preparation for the assessments.

1)   At the end of each lesson, ask your students to restate the concepts taught in the lesson. F example, if they have made a 4 Door Book showing the steps of a process, ask them to tell you about each step using the pictures as a prompt. This assessment can be done by you by a student.

) At the end of each lesson, ask your students to answer the questions on the inside back cover of the *Lots of Science Library Book* for that lesson. The answers to these questions may be given verbally or in writing. Ask older students to use their vocabulary words in context as they answer the questions. This is a far more effective method to determine their knowledge of the vocabulary words than a matching or multiple choice test on the words.

) Provide your students with Plant Concept Maps that are partially completed. Ask them to fill in the blanks. Example for after Lesson 19:

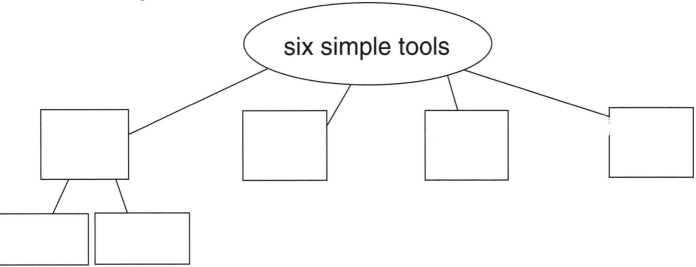

) Use the 3D Graphic Organizers to assess your students' understanding of the concepts. Use the *Tool Concepts* listed on the teachers' pages to determine exactly what you want covered in the assessments. Primary and beginning students may use the pictures found on the Graphics Pages as guides for their assessments. By using the pictures, your students are sequencing and matching while recalling information. Older students should draw their own pictures and use their vocabulary words in their descriptions of the concepts. Below are suggestions for this method of assessment.

  a) Lesson 3 – Make a Large Question and Answer Book. On the left tab, write *Work*. On the right tab, write *Friction*. Under the *work* tab, write the formula for work, the way friction affects work, and how to decrease friction when working. Under the *friction* tab, explain friction, its benefits, and the three types of friction. In this assessment, 10 points can be given for each correct answer and 10 points for extra credit.

  b) Lesson 10 – Make a Layered Look Book. Label the cover *Inclined Planes*. On the first tab, write *inclined planes* and explain the tool and how it is used. On the second tab, write *wedge* and explain the tool and how it is used. On the bottom tab, write *screw* and explain the tool and how it is used.

  c) Lesson 14 – Make a 3 Tab Book. Label the tabs as follows: *class one lever, class two lever, class three lever.* Under each tab, draw a diagram of the lever, label the parts, and explain how it is used.

  d) Lesson 16 – Make a Half Book. Draw a diagram of a wheel and axle on the cover. Inside the book, explain the tool, and how it is used.

  e) Lesson 19 – Make a 3 Tab Book. Label the tabs as follows: *fixed pulley, moveable pulley, compound pulley.* Under each tab, draw a diagram of the pulley, label the parts, and explain how the pulley is used.

  f) Lesson 23 – Make a 4 Door Book. Open the book and label each tab as follows: *gears, cams, cranks, springs.* Under each tab, explain the tool and how it is used.

Notes

Great Science Adventures

Lots of Science Library Books

part of their *Great Science Adventure,* your students will create *Lots of Science Library Books.* Each s *of Science Library Book* is made of 16 pages, plus a front and back cover. All the covers to the s *of Science Library Books* are located at the front of this section. The covers are owed by the inside pages of the books.

How to Photocopy the *Lots of Science Library Books*

e *Lots of Science Library Books* are provided as consumable pages which may be cut out of the at *Science Adventures* book at the line on the top of each page. If, however, you wish to make otocopies for your students, you can do so by following the instructions below.

photocopy the inside pages of the *Lots of Science Library Books:*

Note that there is a "Star" above the line at the top of each *Lots of Science Library Book* sheet.

Locate the *Lots of Science Library Book* sheet that has a Star above page 16 of the book. Position this sheet on the glass of your photocopier so that the side of the sheet that contains page 16 is facing down, and the Star above page 16 is in the left corner closest to you. Photocopy the page.

Turn the *Lots of Science Library Book* sheet over so that the side of the *Lots of Science Library Book* sheet containing page 6 is now face down. Position the sheet so that the Star above page 6 is again in the left corner closest to you.

Insert the previously photocopied paper into the copier again, face down and with the Star at the end of the sheet that enters the copier last. Photocopy the page.

Repeat steps 1 through 4, above, for each *Lots of Science Library Book* sheet.

photocopy the covers of the *Lots of Science Library Books:*

Insert "Cover Sheet A" in the photocopier with a Star positioned in the left corner closest to you, facing down. Photocopy the page.

Turn "Cover Sheet A" over so that the side you just photocopied is now facing you. Position the sheet so that the Star is again in the left corner closest to you, facing down.

Insert the previously photocopied paper into the copier again, face down and with the Star entering the copier last. Photocopy the page.

Repeat steps 1 through 3, above, for Cover Sheets B, C, D, E, and F.

e: The owner of this book has permission to photocopy the *Lots of Science Library Book* pages covers for classroom use only.

How to assemble the *Lots of Science Library Books*

Once you have made the photocopies or cut the consumable pages out of this book, you are read to assemble your *Lots of Science Library Books.* To do so, follow these instructions:

1. Cut each sheet, both covers and inside pages, on the solid lines.

2. Lay the inside pages on top of one another in this order: pages 2 and 15, pages 4 and 13, page and 11, pages 8 and 9.

3. Fold the stacked pages on the dotted line, with pages 8 and 9 facing each other.

4. Turn the pages over so that pages 1 and 16 are on top.

5. Place the appropriate cover pages on top of the inside pages, with the front cover facing up.

6. Staple on the dotted line in two places.

You now have completed *Lots of Science Library Books.*

What is a tool?

Lots of Science Library Book #4

What are the types of friction?

Lots of Science Library Book #3

What is friction?

Lots of Science Library Book #2

What is work?

Lots of Science Library Book #1

tool
machine
effort
magnify
direction

* mechanical advantage
* complex machine
* input force
* output force

starting friction
sliding friction
rolling friction

Describe the three
types of friction.

Explain how tools
make work easier.

work
force
distance
weight
load

* motion
* formula
* physics

surface
friction
increase
decrease
wheels
liquid

* lubrication

Describe work.
Explain two ways
work can be increased.

Describe friction.
Explain how friction
affects work.

List two ways to
decrease friction.

How do we use wedges?

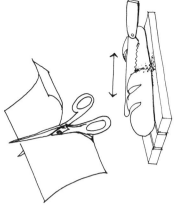

What is a wedge?

How do we use inclined planes?

What is an inclined plane?

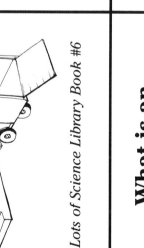

plow
zipper
slide
* titanium

wedge
thick
thin
pointed
tapers
* resistant

Explain how wedges
are used today.

Describe a wedge.

Explain how this
tool uses force.

board
direction

inclined plane
slanted

Explain how to
increase the
mechanical advantage
of an inclined plane.

Describe an
inclined plane.

Explain how this
tool uses force.

What is a class one lever?

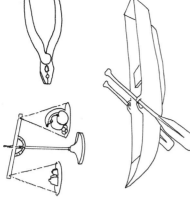

What is a lever?

fulcrum

rod

How do we use screws?

What is a screw?

class one lever
seesaw
load
* measurements
* accurate

rotate
lever
fulcrum
bar
rod
* pivot point
* fixed point

Describe a
class one lever.

List examples of
class one levers.

Describe a lever.

Explain how this tool
uses force.

faucet
drill
vice
nuts
bolts

* complicated

screw
attach
cylinder
* thread
* pitch
* cast
* foundry

Describe Archimedes' screw.

Explain how screws
are used today.

Describe a screw.

Explain how this
tool uses force.

How do we use the wheel and axle?

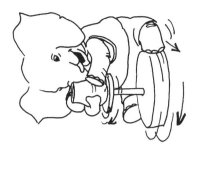

What is a wheel and axle?

What is a class three lever?

What is a class two lever?

shaft
input force
output force
* accuracy

Explain how wheels
and axles are
used today.

class three lever

* elaborate
* efficient
* factory

Describe a class
three lever.

List examples of
class three levers.

wheel and axle
water wheel

* Industrial Revolution
* mass production

Describe a wheel
and axle.

Explain how this
tool uses forces.

class two lever

* composite

Describe a class
two lever.

List examples of
class two levers.

What are the six simple tools?

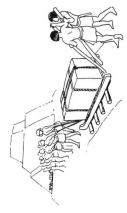

What is a compound pulley?

What is a moveable pulley?

What is a fixed pulley?

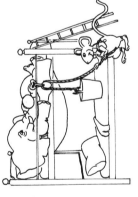

List the six
simple tools.

compound pulley
force load
magnifies

* electric power
* artisan

Describe a
compound pulley.

Explain how this
tool uses forces.

moveable pulley

* internal combustion engine
* jet engine

pulley
wheel
rope
load distance
effort distance
fixed pulley

Describe a
fixed pulley.

Explain how this
tool uses forces.
* artisan

Describe a
moveable pulley.

Explain how this
tool uses forces.

How are tools powered?

Lots of Science Library Book #24

What is a spring?

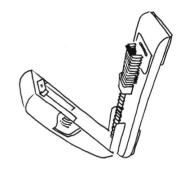

Lots of Science Library Book #23

What are cams and cranks?

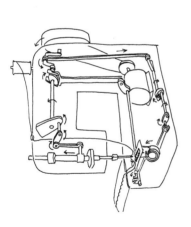

Lots of Science Library Book #22

What are gears?

Lots of Science Library Book #21

technology
power
simple tools
complex machines
steam engine
gasoline engine
diesel engine

Explain how tools are powered.

cam
crank
hinged
crankshaft
* diagnostic

Describe cams and cranks.
Explain how these tools use forces.

spring
position
energy
stapler
absorb
* torsion bar

Describe a spring.
Explain how springs use forces.

gears
cog
spur gear
rack and pinion
bevel gears
worm gears
* microchips

Describe gears.
Explain how gears use force.

5

7

More work is required to move a heavy load the same distance as a lighter load.

12   Lots of Science Library Book #1

Now, Max can move Elmer by tickling him.

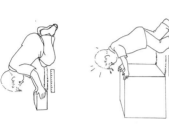

10   Lots of Science Library Book #1

Meet Max the mouse and his buddy, Elmer the elephant.

1   Lots of Science Library Book #1

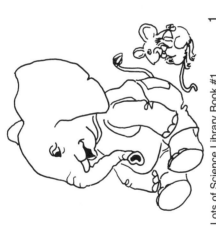

3   Lots of Science Library Book #1

Tools in Time

4500 B.C. Yugoslavia

Fishermen near the Black Sea in the region of Yugoslavia area used fishhooks to catch their food.

16   Lots of Science Library Book #1

Scientists measure work by multiplying the force, or weight, of the load by the distance the load is moved. So the formula for work is force x distance = work.

10 pounds

2 feet

10 pounds moved (x) 2 feet = 20 foot-pounds.

14   Lots of Science Library Book #1

Even though Max is tired, he has not done any work. It might be hard to convince Max of that fact, though. In order for work to take place, a force must act on an object, or load, and move it. A force is either a push or a pull. Elmer did not move, so no work was done.

Two things must happen for work to take place:
1) An object, or load, must move
2) A force must be used in the direction of the motion.

6
Lots of Science Library Book #1

What work have you done today? Remember that work is done when a force is applied to an object, or load, to make it move.

11

Elmer likes to listen to music. When he listens to music, he does not pay attention to what is going on around him. So while Elmer is enjoying his music, he does not know that he is sitting on Max's tail.

2
Lots of Science Library Book #1

Tools in Time

6000 B.C.   Jordan

Farmers used a sickle to cut crops. This sickle was made of bone and had flint teeth.

15

8
Physics is the study of the properties of matter and energy.

Lots of Science Library Book #1

Now Max is working. Although the feather is lightweight, Max is using force to move the feather. Since the feather moved by the force Max used on it, he did work.

9

Max is trying very hard to get Elmer off his tail. Max is using all the force he has to move Elmer, but Elmer does not move.

4
Lots of Science Library Book #1

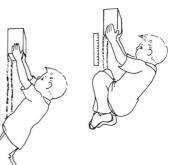

More work is required to move a load a farther distance than the same load a shorter distance.

13

5

There are two ways to reduce friction so work can be done more easily. One is by using lubrication. Putting certain liquids on a surface can reduce friction, making work easier.

Lots of Science Library Book #2   12

Have you ever had very cold hands? Even without a heater, you can create heat to warm your hands. Do you know how?

Lots of Science Library Book #2   1

Tools in Time

700 B.C.   Europe

Horseshoes were made and used by farmers and warriors.

16

7

Do you remember how we define work? Work takes place when a force acts on an object, or load, to make it move. Friction can be a problem when Max is trying to work.

Lots of Science Library Book #2

10

The rough parts of surfaces, no matter how small, catch on each other and create friction when they rub on one another. The rougher the surface, the more friction is created.

Lots of Science Library Book #2   3

Friction occurs because no surface is perfectly smooth.

Another way to reduce friction is with the use of wheels, or ball bearings. Putting a load on wheels reduces friction. By reducing friction, we can do work with less force.

Lots of Science Library Book #2   14

Friction is very helpful to us. Friction is what makes a car stop when the brakes are applied. The brakes rubbing against the wheels create enough friction to stop the car.

Lots of Science Library Book #2

When the hill is covered with grass, there is more friction. With the increase in friction, Max must use more force to move Elmer down the hill.

Lots of Science Library Book #2

Tools in Time

6000 B.C. France

Hunters used stone spearheads attached to wooden shafts.

Basketball shoes create enough friction so a player can run easily on a basketball court. Because of friction, the player can stop without sliding.

By rubbing your hands together, you create heat. The force that creates the heat is called friction.

Lots of Science Library Book #2

When Max pushes Elmer down an icy hill, there is not much friction. The less friction there is, the less force Max needs to move Elmer down the hill.

Lots of Science Library Book #2

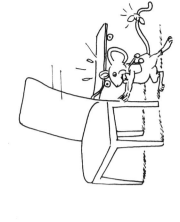

There is less friction when an object is in motion. This is called sliding motion.

5

7

In both starting and sliding motion, the amount of friction depends on the force pressing between the two objects, or surfaces. The amount of friction depends partly upon the weight of the object being moved.

12   Lots of Science Library Book #3

Max places wheels under the chair so he can roll it. The wheels reduce friction and make the chair easier to move. Now he can use less force to do the work. This is called rolling friction.

10   Lots of Science Library Book #3

Remember, friction occurs when surfaces rub against each other. Friction can be helpful, but when we are working, it can create a need for more force to complete the work.

1   Lots of Science Library Book #3

3   Lots of Science Library Book #3

WHO'S· WHO

Isaac Newton discovered many things about forces, motion, and energy. He is credited with writing The Three Laws of Motion:
1. A body at rest will remain at rest unless an outside force acts upon it.
2. A change in the motion of a body depends upon how much mass there is and how much force is acting upon it.
3. For every action, there is an equal and opposite reaction.

16   Lots of Science Library Book #3

When Elmer pushes Max, there is less friction because the weight of the load is less.

14   Lots of Science Library Book #3

Although friction is reduced with sliding motion, Max still has to use a great amount of force to move the chair. Then Max thinks of a better idea.

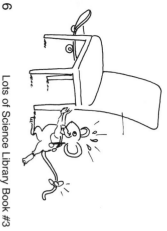

Friction between two surfaces is the greatest just before the load moves. This is called starting friction.

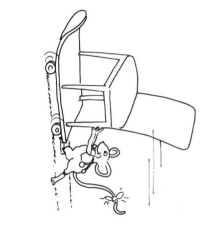

Poor Max has a sore tail. To save his tail from any more injury, Max decides to move a chair into the room for Elmer to sit on. The chair is heavy, but Max finally begins to move it.

As the chair begins to move, Max is surprised to discover that it is easier to continue moving the chair than it was to start moving the chair. Max just learned two things about friction.

When Max pushes Elmer, there is a great deal of friction because the weight of the load is great.

Tools in Time

1000 B.C.

Northern Europe

The use of wooden ball bearings on wheels decreased friction and made carts roll easily.

By using a car jack, you can lift a car easily with your hands.

5

By using a can opener, you can easily open a can with your hands.

7

Tools also change the direction of the force. By applying force in different directions, tools help us to complete work.

12

All the helpful items used to complete work are called tools. A tool makes work easier because it changes the force applied to the work.

10

We have learned that work occurs when force is applied to a load to make it move. A force can be a push or a pull. Work can require a small amount of force or a great amount of force.

1

By using a hammer to remove the nail, you can easily do the work with one hand.

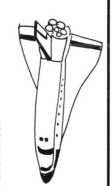

3

TECHNOLOGY

Technology is the art and science of making things useful in our everyday lives. It includes the use of tools, machines, and materials to help us live and work efficiently. Technology involves looking for needs in life, designing ways to meet those needs, and valuing accidental discoveries.

16

There are six basic tools: inclined plane, wedge, screw, lever, wheel and axle, and pulley. Anything that uses two or more of these tools is called a complex machine.

14

Can you create enough force with your hands to chop down a tree?

At lunchtime, can you open a can with your hands? A great amount of force is required to open the can. Can you produce enough force to do that work?

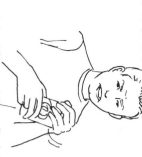

By using an axe, you can more easily do the work of cutting down the tree.

Tools help us to magnify our force. They help us to do work that we could not do with our own strength.

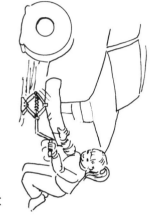

To remove a nail from a piece of wood, you would need a lot of force. Can you produce enough force with your fingers to remove the nail?

To change a flat tire requires force to lift the car. Can you create enough force with your arms to lift a car?

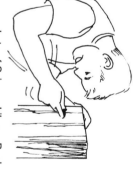

The amount of effort we save by using a tool is called its mechanical advantage. Input force is the force exerted on a machine. Output force is the force exerted on a load by a machine.

$$\text{Mechanical Advantage} = \frac{\text{Output Force}}{\text{Input Force}}$$

By using a tool, we can do work with less force, or effort.

Tools in Time

250 A.D.
Roman Empire

Farmers used ox-drawn plows to till soil on their farms.

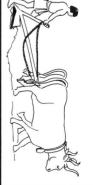

TECHNOLOGY

Finding ways to change simple materials into useful items is another form of technology. For example, soft clay can be easily formed into a pot, but the pot would be too fragile to use for many purposes. However, this fragile item can be transformed with fire. By heating the soft clay, we can create a hard, waterproof pot that can be used for cooking or storing food.

16

Max and Elmer share a room.

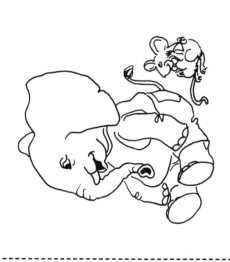

1

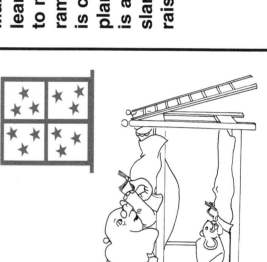

3

So Max must help Elmer get up to the top bunk. Max is little, and Elmer is big and heavy. How can Max help Elmer get to the top bunk?

5

7

Pushing Elmer up the inclined plane took effort for Max. He had to use force. But the amount of force he used was much less than if he had lifted Elmer straight up to the top bunk.

14

Max finds a board and leans it against the bed to make a ramp. The ramp that Max is making is called an inclined plane. An inclined plane is a simple tool. It is a slanted surface used to raise an object.

10

With the inclined plane, Max uses less force to push Elmer, the load, up the ramp than it takes to lift Elmer straight up to the top bunk. The inclined plane magnifies Max's force so he can do work that he could not do otherwise.

12

Max tries to push Elmer up the ladder, but he cannot move Elmer. Max does not have enough force to push a load as heavy as Elmer up to the top bunk. How can Max help Elmer get up to the top bunk?

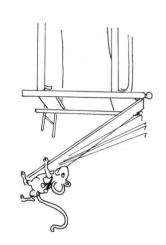

Then Max gets an idea.

Max is very tired, but no work has been done because Elmer, the load, did not move.

Max is afraid of heights so he likes to sleep on the bottom bunk. Elmer likes to sleep on the top bunk to be near the stars.

Tools in Time

6000 B.C.   Jericho

Wealthy residents used ladders to get to the roofs of their houses. The ladders were placed in an inclined position to make the climb easier.

Today, Elmer has a very sore toe and cannot walk.

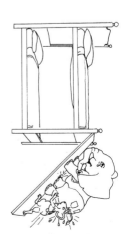

The ideal mechanical advantage of this inclined plane is 10 divided by 5 = 2. This number can be used to compare the mechanical advantages of different inclined planes.

Friction is present when using an inclined plane. Do you have any ideas how Max could reduce the friction when pushing Elmer to the top bunk?

12   Lots of Science Library Book #6

The amount of work is the same with both ramps, but the longer ramp allows work to be done with less work.

10   Lots of Science Library Book #6

An inclined plane has no moving parts; yet, it is a tool. Remember that a tool is anything that changes the amount or direction of forces acting upon it.

Lots of Science Library Book #6   1

3

TECHNOLOGY

The first plastic was invented by Alexander Parkes in about 1855. This material was eventually improved upon in the United States and became the material that made movies possible. This early plastic was the beginning of a revolution in technology that now touches every part of our lives.

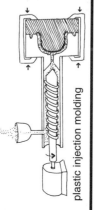

plastic injection molding

16   Lots of Science Library Book #6

Even a road that winds around a mountain is an inclined plane. If you imagine taking the road off the mountain and laying it out flat, the road would form a large inclined plane.

14   Lots of Science Library Book #6

Using a tool to do work gives Max a mechanical advantage. That means that the tool allows him to do work with less effort.

To determine the ideal mechanical advantage for an inclined plane, divide the length of the board by the height of the incline. Here is the formula:

Ideal Mech. Adv. = $\dfrac{\text{Length of board}}{\text{Height of the incline}}$

If Max used a longer board for his inclined plane and kept the height the same, the mechanical advantage would be greater. With the longer ramp, Max could use less force to get Elmer to the top bunk, but it would be a longer distance for Max to push Elmer.

Elmer gets to the top bunk when either inclined plane is used, but Max is not as tired when he uses the longer one.

The formula for the mechanical advantage is called "ideal" because friction is always a factor that lessens the mechanical advantage. Therefore, we calculate what the advantage would be without friction under ideal conditions.

11

The ideal mechanical advantage of this inclined plane is 15 divided by 5 = 3. Compare this number with the previous inclined plane. This inclined plane has a higher ideal mechanical advantage.

9

Without the inclined plane, Max could not have lifted Elmer to the top bunk. Max did not have the force needed to do that work.

An inclined plane spreads the force out over a longer distance. Max had to push Elmer a longer distance and it took more time than if he had lifted Elmer straight up. However, Max used less effort than he would have without the inclined plane.

The force used to push a load on an inclined plane is called the input force.

4

We use inclined planes every day.

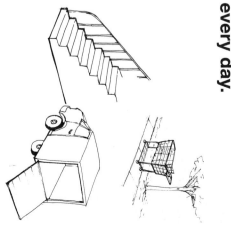

A staircase is a slight variation of the inclined plane.

13

Tools in Time

3500 B.C.
Mesopotamia

Copper nails were used by people for building.

15

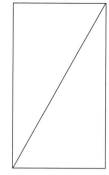

5

Max remembers the inclined plane that helped him get Elmer to the top bunk. He finds a block of wood and draws an inclined plane on the wood.

An axe is an example of a wedge. By applying force to the thick end of the axe, the force is magnified into the wood. The force also changes direction by creating a sideways force splitting the wood.

Now Max can use the wedge tool to magnify his force. This tool will also change the direction of his force. When he applies force to the thick end of the wedge, the force pushes out to the pointed end, creating a "sideways" force.

Do you remember when Max moved Elmer's chair, using a skateboard? The wheels on the skateboard reduced the friction, making it easier for Max to move the chair.

TECHNOLOGY

Rearranging materials to suit the needs of man is an important part of technology. One aspect is rearranging or separating things that are joined together, such as cutting a branch from a tree. Certain kinds of stone, such as flint and obsidian, are strong enough to cut materials and can be easily sharpened. However, metals make better cutting tools because they are strong and do not crack easily.

Tools help us to work by magnifying force and changing the direction of the force. The wedge is a very useful tool, just ask Max.

Then Max gets an idea.

6

Lots of Science Library Book #7

By cutting on the line, Max makes a wedge. A wedge has a thick end that tapers down to a thin, pointed end. The wedge is a simple tool.

8

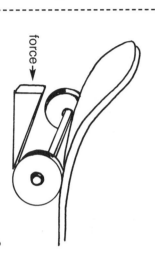

thick end

thin pointed end

Lots of Science Library Book #7

When force is applied to the thick end of the wedge, the pointed end will go under or into an object.

9

force→

11

Now Max has another problem to solve. Elmer likes to sit up high in the chair while it is on the skateboard. Every time Elmer breathes, the skateboard moves. Max can only imagine how much it would hurt if his tail got caught under the wheels.

2

Lots of Science Library Book #7

Max tries to stop the skateboard from moving by using his own force. He uses all his effort to hold the skateboard still, but he cannot do it for very long.

4

Lots of Science Library Book #7

13

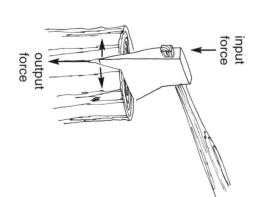

input force

output force

Tools in Time

400 B.C.   China

Farmers used iron plows to plant crops.

15

The ideal mechanical advantage of a wedge is found by dividing the length of the wedge by the width of the thick end of the wedge. The formula for the mechanical advantage is:

$$\text{Ideal Mech. Adv.} = \frac{\text{Length of Wedge}}{\text{Width of Thick End}}$$

---

1. The first wedge of a plow, the coulter, slices a furrow in the soil.
2. The next wedge, the share, cuts loose the top layer of soil.
3. The final wedge, the moldboard, lifts and turns the top layer of soil. This work breaks up the soil for planting seeds and buries old vegetation so it can rot and provide nutrients for the new plants.

Also in the slide is a set of two wedges that close the zipper.

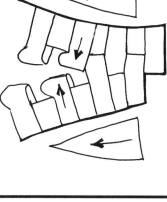

Borrowing some of the ideas of Elias Howe, the inventor of the sewing machine, Judson invented the "slide fastener," a prototype of today's zipper. The slide fastener allowed his friend to "zip" up his shoes with one easy stroke.

A wedge is a useful tool. It has a thick end that tapers down to a thin, pointed end. A wedge magnifies force and changes the direction of the force.

Friction is helpful when using a wedge. Friction holds the wedge in place.

TECHNOLOGY

Finding and using strong materials is an important part of technology. Metals offer an impressive blend of strength, toughness, and stiffness, making them useful as cutting tools. Metals can also be transformed into many different shapes, making them useful in many areas of our lives. Metals have been essential to the transportation revolution—from railroads using iron to the aerospace program using titanium.

Tools in Time

3000 B.C.   Egypt

Builders used saws to cut wood as well as stone.

A plow is one wedge that has been used for thousands of years. A plow uses several wedges to prepare soil for planting.

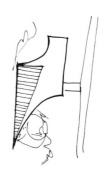

Inside the slide of a zipper, a wedge pushes the zipper teeth apart.

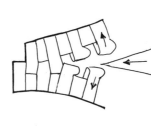

We use wedges every day. Can you name some tools that are wedges?

Whitcomb L. Judson, a Chicago engineer, invented many things. He improved various motors and the railroad braking systems. When a friend came to him for help, Judson took on the challenge. His friend had a stiff back, so that he could not tie his shoelaces.

Judson thought of a way to make a fastener that could be used with only one hand. Can you guess which fastener he invented?

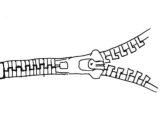

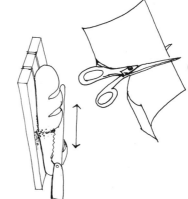

We use wedges every day. Can you name some tools that are wedges?

The longer and thinner the pointed end of a wedge is, the more the force applied to the thick end will be magnified. A long, pointed end means that more distance is required to get the work done, but the increase in force can make it worthwhile for certain work.

Tools in Time

1000 B.C.
Europe and Asia

Scissors were used to cut paper and thread.

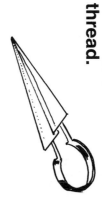

The invention was called the zipper because of the sound it made when opening and closing. Z-Z-Z-I-P!

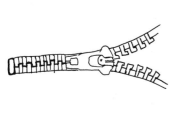

Max decides to use a screw to do this work.

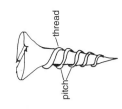

inclined plane

thread

pitch

Screws will give Max a mechanical advantage. We use screws every day.

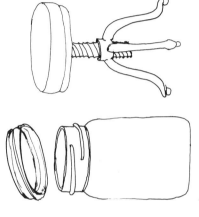

12   Lots of Science Library Book #9

A screw must be turned many times to make it move a short distance. A screw magnifies force, while time and distance are required to complete the work.

10   Lots of Science Library Book #9

Max has used two simple tools to make his work easier. With the inclined plane and the wedge, Max has been able to do work that he could not have done without them.

1

Lots of Science Library Book #9

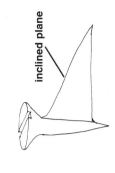

3

Lots of Science Library Book #9

TECHNOLOGY

Metals can be shaped in more ways than most other materials. Metals can be heated to a red-hot liquid and poured into a cast to make various objects. Metals have been molded in this fashion since they were first discovered. The place where metals are molded is called a foundry.

16   Lots of Science Library Book #9

Tools in Time

1450 B.C.   Mesopotamia

Seed drills were used by farmers to plant their crops.

14   Lots of Science Library Book #9

A screw will magnify the turning force applied to its top. A screw moves into wood with greater force than the force it takes to turn it. Friction helps screws to do their work.

A screw is a simple tool. It is an inclined plane wrapped around a cylinder. The spiral around the screw is called the thread. The spiral distance between the threads is the pitch of the screw.

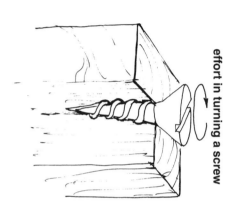

effort in turning a screw

Max needs something that will hold the chair securely to the skateboard. He has an idea.

Now Max has another problem, and these tools will not help him to solve it. Remember how Elmer likes to sit in his chair on the skateboard? Well, Max found a way to keep the skateboard still, but now the chair falls off the skateboard every time Elmer gets in or out of the chair.

The ideal mechanical advantage can be determined by dividing the distance to complete one turn of the screw by the distance between two threads.

Ideal Mechanical Advantage = Distance to complete one turn / Distance between two threads

---

Tools in Time

1405 A.D.   Europe

Metal screws were used by builders.

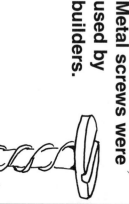

Nuts and bolts use screws to provide the force to hold things in place. A corkscrew can do work that we cannot do on our own. Jars and bottles depend on screws to make a tight seal. Even a vice uses a screw.

The combine harvester is one of the most important inventions in farming. Today's harvester still uses Archimedes' screw.

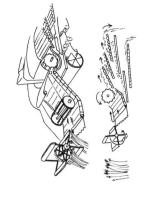

Screws are used in many other tools, as well. Look at a drill. The working part of a drill is a screw. Whether a drill is powered by your hand or by a motor, the screw does the drilling work.

A screw is a simple tool that makes our work easier, just ask Max.

TECHNOLOGY

The products of technology are generally made by joining pieces of materials together. This is necessary because different parts of a product may be made from different materials. Sometimes the product is too large to be made as one piece, such as a building, or it is too complicated to be made as one piece, such as a watch. Therefore, joining materials together is an important feature of technology.

Tools in Time

1250 A.D.   France

The screw-jack, hand-operated tool, was used to lift and support heavy objects.

The force and power of screws can be experienced easily with a water faucet. Turn on a water faucet and see if you can stop the water with your finger.

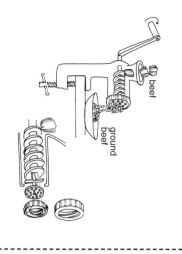

beef

ground beef

Another use of Archimedes' screw is found in a meat grinder.

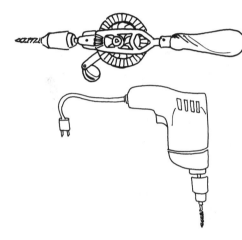

Screws have been used for thousands of years. Archimedes, born in 298 B.C. in Sicily, was a great scientist and mathematician. As a true scientist, he saw the importance of experimentation to test his observations and theories.

While in Egypt, Archimedes invented a mechanical water pump, known today as Archimedes' screw. This device consisted of a large, continuous screw inside a cylinder. The lower end was placed in the river, and as the spiral threads were turned, the water was raised.

Tools in Time

150 B.C.   Greece

Screw tools were used to extract oil from olives and juice from grapes.

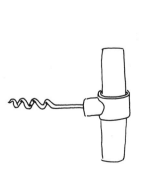

5

Now that Max has lifted Elmer off the flowers, he can rotate the rod on the fulcrum and put Elmer on the ground. The fulcrum does not move, but the rod can rotate to move the force in a different direction.

When the lever rotates on the fulcrum, the fulcrum is known as the pivot-point.

12   Lots of Science Library Book #11

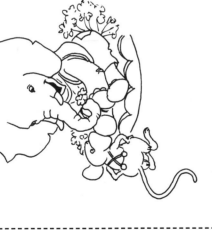

7

Levers, like other simple tools, help us to do our work with less effort. The lever has two parts. One part is a bar or rod. It moves when work is being done. The second part is the fulcrum. It does not move when work is being done.

The fulcrum is called a fixed point.

10   Lots of Science Library Book #11

Elmer loves to smell the flowers in the garden.

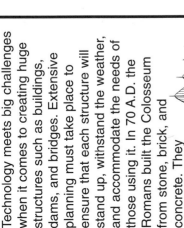

1   Lots of Science Library Book #11

TECHNOLOGY

Technology meets big challenges when it comes to creating huge structures such as buildings, dams, and bridges. Extensive planning must take place to ensure that each structure will stand up, withstand the weather, and accommodate the needs of those using it. In 70 A.D. the Romans built the Colosseum from stone, brick, and concrete. They were the first to use concrete on such a large scale.

16   Lots of Science Library Book #11

3

Tools in Time

1500 B.C.   Egypt Farmers drew water to irrigate their fields. A counterweight attached to the opposite end of a beam made it easier for workers to lift the water.

14   Lots of Science Library Book #11

The lever has a positive mechanical advantage.

Elmer is the load on one end of the lever. Max is the effort on the other end of the lever. Although Elmer weighs a great deal, Max can move him with the magnified force of the lever.

Max uses a shovel to lift Elmer off the flowers. The spoon part of the shovel acts like a wedge between the load Elmer, and the garden. The handle of the shovel acts like the rod of a lever.

To raise the load, the effort on the opposite end of the lever must move farther than the load rises.

Max gets an idea. Max hurries to find something he can use as a lever. The lever is a simple tool used to make work easier to complete.

Max does not like to have Elmer sit on the flowers. Max tries to push Elmer off the flowers, but Elmer, the load, is too heavy. Max tries to pull Elmer off the flowers, but Elmer, the load, is still too heavy.

Tools in Time

1650 B.C.   Greece

Bronze swords were used by warriors.

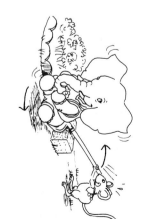

load

rod

fulcrum

effort

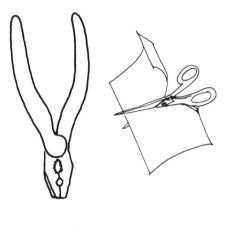

Max and Elmer love to play at the park.

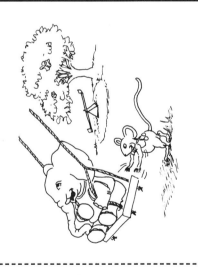

T E C H N O L O G Y

Accurate measurements are extremely important for technology. When a product, such as a car, is made of thousands of parts that could come from all over the world, accurate measurements are essential. Mechanical parts need to be accurate to within 0.0001 of an inch (0.025 mm). For radios and satellites to work, time must be measured accurately to within less than a second per century.

Force is applied to the other side of the rod. This side is called the effort arm.

Scientists can determine the amount of force needed to lift a load with a class one lever by using a formula.

input force

force applied to lever

work force from lever

load

output force

fulcrum

Load x Length of Load Arm = Effort x Length of Effort Arm

Tools in Time

2500 B.C.   Egypt

Men cut grain using flint sickles.

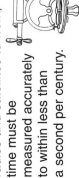

The fulcrum divides the lever into two sides. One side of the rod holds the load. This is called the load arm.

6

8

If the fulcrum is moved closer to the load or the load moves closer to the fulcrum, this decreases the amount of force needed to lift the load. So when Max's cousins have to go home, Max asks Elmer to move closer to the middle of the seesaw, or closer to the fulcrum.

Class one levers are used everyday.

11

Elmer sits on one end of the seesaw. Max tries to lift Elmer, but Elmer, the load, is too heavy for Max to lift. Then Max gets an idea.

2

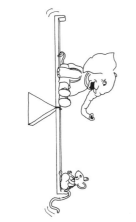

9

Max asks his cousins to sit on his side of the seesaw. With Max and his cousins on one side, there is enough force to lift Elmer off the ground.

The seesaw is an example of a class one lever. Class one levers consist of a rod, fulcrum, load, and effort.

4

Tools in Time

2000 B.C.   Egypt

Large boats, 140 feet in length, were powered by huge oars and an elaborate steering system.

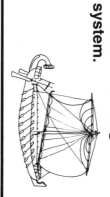

Archimedes said, "Give me a long enough lever and a place to stand, and I will move the earth."

15

13

---

fulcrum

load

force or effect

force or effect

All class two levers magnify force, but distance and speed are lessened.

output force

load

work force from lever

fulcrum

force applied to lever

input force

Scientists can determine the amount of force needed to lift a load with a class two lever by using this formula: Load x Length of Load Arm = Effort x Length of Effort Arm

---

The class two lever has the fulcrum at one end, the effort at the other end, and the load in between. The effort and the load move in the same direction, so there is no changing of directions with the class two lever.

fulcrum

load

effort

effort

Max finds some nuts and wants to share them with his buddy, Elmer. The nuts have a hard shell and Max cannot open them.

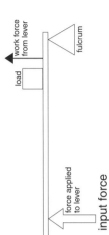

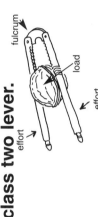

TECHNOLOGY

Materials can often be improved by putting two together. These composite materials are usually made from a pair of materials that have opposite properties. A strong but flexible material may be combined with a weak but firm material to create a strong, firm material. For example, fibers of carbon, a very stiff and lightweight material, are mixed with nylon, a tough plastic, creating the material called graphite. Graphite is used to create sturdy, lightweight sports equipment.

Tools in Time

1220 A.D.   Northern Europe

Wooden wheelbarrow were used to carry heavy loads.

The nutcracker is an example of a class two lever. A class two lever always has the fulcrum on one end with the force applied on the other end. In the nutcracker, the nut is the load. The load is placed between the fulcrum and the effort.

6

8

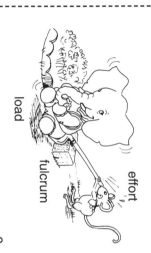

Look at the class one lever and the class two lever. How are they alike? How do they differ?

Both the class one lever and the class two lever magnify force. Both of these levers require less force to work when the effort arms are longer. Although the longer levers use less force, one's arm must move farther to do the work.

11

9

The class one lever has the fulcrum between the effort and the load. Since the lever can rotate, the force can change directions.

effort

fulcrum

load

2

Elmer tries to open the nuts, but, their shells are too hard. Elmer does not have enough force to open them. This time Elmer gets an idea, and he looks for the right tool to do this work.

4

Elmer finds a nutcracker and gives it to Max. Using the nutcracker, Max can easily open the nuts. The nutcracker makes the work easier because it is a simple tool.

13

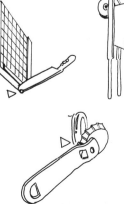

Other simple machines that use class two levers are wheelbarrows, paper cutters, and bottle openers.

15

Tools in Time

2800 B.C.   China

Rope was made from hemp plants.

fulcrum

effort

load

We have learned about three different types of levers. Complex machines use these levers to make our work easier.

12   Lots of Science Library Book #14

We use class three levers every day.

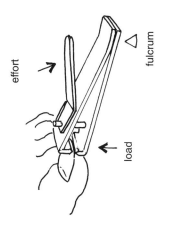

effort

fulcrum

load

10   Lots of Science Library Book #14

Max and Elmer look forward to fall, when the leaves are colorful and the air is cool.

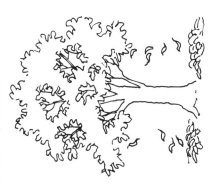

1

Lots of Science Library Book #14

3

Lots of Science Library Book #14

TECHNOLOGY

Communication is one of our most useful skills, but it can be greatly limited without technology. For thousands of years, a book could be reproduced only if copied by hand. This was time consuming, making books rare and expensive. The printing press made written communication much easier. Distant speech communication became possible with the invention of the telephone in 1876 by Alexander Graham Bell. Technology continues to play a major role in worldwide communication systems.

16   Lots of Science Library Book #14

Tools in Time

1040 A.D.   China

Pi Sheng invented printing using moveable type. The raised letters were arranged on an iron frame.

14   Lots of Science Library Book #14

The effort in a class three lever is placed between the fulcrum and the load. The class three lever of the rake reduces force, but increases the distance moved. Max's rake reaches farther than his hand. This lets him reach more leaves, so that Max can do more work with less effort.

Max pushes and pulls the rake with his lower hand. The fan of the rake applies force to the leaves which are the load. This force is not magnified in strength, but it is magnified in distance. Using the same amount of force, Max can move more leaves with a rake than with his hands.

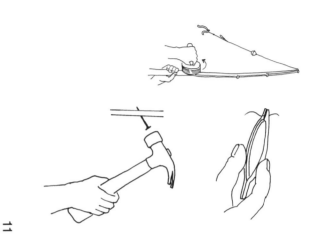

11

This diagram shows how force is used in a class three lever.

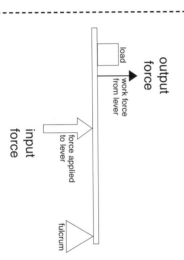

output force

work force from lever

input force

force applied to lever

load

fulcrum

9

A rake is an example of a class three lever. As Max rakes leaves, the fulcrum is beside the wrist of his upper hand. The fulcrum of a class three lever is always at one end of the rod.

2

Fall is a good time to play outside. The weather is cool and the air smells fresh. It is also a time to work in the yard since leaves are falling off the trees.

13

Tools in Time

1450 A.D.   Germany

Johann Gutenberg invented the printing press.
By 1500, over 8 million books had been printed.

15

5

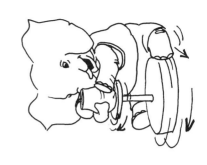

7

A water wheel is another example of a wheel and axle. Water wheels were used to grind grain. Later, they were used in factories to generate power.

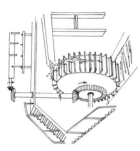

12

Lots of Science Library Book #15

The wheel and axle magnifies force. The wheel and axle is a simple tool. A small turning force applied to the wheel produces an increased turning force on the axle.

10

Lots of Science Library Book #15

Max likes to ride his bicycle.

1

Lots of Science Library Book #15

Without the wheel and axle, they could not ride vehicles. The wheel and axle is used in all modes of transportation, like bicycles, cars, trucks, trains, and airplanes.

3

Lots of Science Library Book #15

TECHNOLOGY

The water wheel gave the Industrial Revolution of the late 18th century the power to succeed. Water wheels were installed in textile factories to power the spinning machines and looms. For the first time, products that previously had only been made by hand could be mass produced. As cloth became mass-produced garments became much cheaper to buy.

16 Lots of Science Library Book #15

Tools in Time

3200 B.C.   Iraq
Solid wooden wheels were used on wagons and carts.

14 Lots of Science Library Book #15

8

Look at a potter's wheel. A potter's wheel consists of two wheels. Elmer's foot moves the bottom wheel. When the bottom wheel turns, the top wheel turns, too.

6

The top wheel is where Elmer makes the pot. The top wheel is called the axle. When the wheel turns, the axle turns.

11

With the use of the wheel and axle, heavy loads can be moved with less effort. For example this tool is used to make the steering wheel of a car.

When the axle turns, the wheel turns.

9

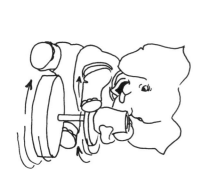

Although the wheel is used for transportation, its greatest function is to reduce friction, or dragging force. As a wheel rolls, a point of its rim touches the ground and moves up. If wheels did not roll, their rims would drag, creating a great amount of friction.

4

2

Elmer likes to ride his tricycle.

Tools in Time

2000 B.C.   India Europe

Lighter wheels were made with a hub, axle, wooden spokes, and a wooden rim.

15

Tools in Time

1000 B.C.   Greece

A potter's wheel was used to make storage jars, cooking pots, and lamps.

13

The water wheel also shows how a wheel and axle works. Unlike the screwdriver, this tool produces more force at the axle, which increases the speed and distance.

When the axle turns the wheel, it becomes a class three lever. The fulcrum is at the center of the axle. The radius of the wheel becomes the load arm. The radius of the axle becomes the effort arm.

There are two ways to create a product: One person can complete all the steps involved in the process; or several people can complete it, with each person doing one part of the process. The second way is called mass production. When the creation of a product is broken down into simple steps, a machine or worker can do the work very quickly. Also, the parts of the product become interchangeable. Eli Whitney made 10,000 muskets for the American army in this manner. The parts were made with such accuracy that each part could fit any musket.

The shaft of the screwdriver is the axle. The wheel turns the axle.

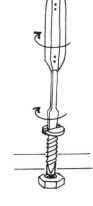

When the wheel is turning the axle, it is a form of a class two lever. The fulcrum is at the center of the axle.

With force a screwdriver can drive a screw into a piece of wood, but it takes time to turn the screwdriver and requires distance to make the screw turn.

This tool increases force, but decreases speed and distance.

Elmer loves to ride his tricycle.

Tools in Time

900 A.D.   Europe

Wheeled plows made farming easier.

A screwdriver shows how a wheel and axle works. The handle of a screwdriver is the wheel. It magnifies the turning force.

A doorknob is another common example of a wheel and axle.

wheel

axle

When it does not work properly, he is unhappy. Elmer is trying to fix his tricycle right now. He is upset because he cannot get the screw in the correct place.

Scientists can measure the ideal mechanical advantage of the wheel and axle.

Ideal Mech. Adv. = $\dfrac{\text{Radius of wheel}}{\text{Radius of axle}}$

The force that Elmer uses to turn the handle of the screwdriver, or the wheel, is called the input force. This is the force that Elmer applies to the work. This makes the shaft, or the axle, turn the screw.

The force that turns the screw is called the output force. It is the force the tool uses to complete the work.

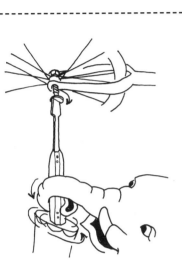

Max gets a screwdriver to help Elmer do his work. After Max shows Elmer how to use the screwdriver, Elmer fixes his tricycle.

Tools in Time

900 B.C.   Assyria

War chariots had spoked wheels made of iron that made them faster and easy to control.

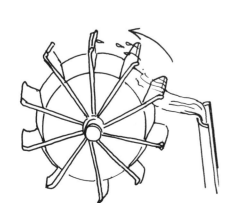

When Max pulls on the rope of the fixed pulley, the bucket rises. The pulley changes the direction of the input force.

When you pull down on a fixed pulley, the load rises. The pulley changes the direction of the input force. This is the same thing that happens with a class one lever but force is applied to a rope instead of a rod. The center of the wheel acts like a fulcrum.

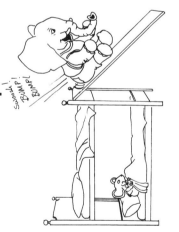

The force you exert on the rope is the effort. The distance the rope is pulled down is the effort distance.

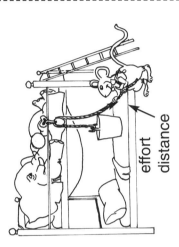

effort distance

Elmer gets thirsty one night and wants a drink of water. The bed shakes when Elmer gets down, which wakes up Max.

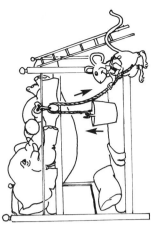

SWOOSH! BUMP! BUMP!

The bucket of water, or the load, is attached to one end of the rope. The other end of the rope is pulled to move the load.

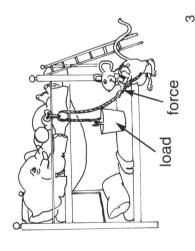

load   force

TECHNOLOGY

As technology produced more elaborate tools and machines, man completed more work with less effort. Josiah Wedgwood, who lived in England between 1730 – 1795, was one of the first people to organize workers for more efficient production. He installed a steam engine in a factory to enable many workers to take advantage of the engines power. Josiah Wedgwood also developed unique kinds of pottery. He is best known for his famous Wedgwood blue Jasperware.

Tools in Time

10 B.C.   Rome

Cranes were used by architects in Rome to build large structures.

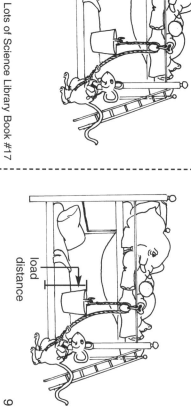

Fixed pulleys are used for opening curtains blinds and in raising a sail.

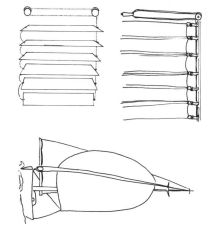

The weight of the object being lifted is called a load. The distance it rises is called the load distance.

load
distance

Like the inclined plane and the lever, the pulley allows a small amount of effort to move a large load. A fixed pulley can have more than one wheel in its system.

Max decides to attach a pulley to the side of the bed. When Max pulls down on the rope, the bucket moves up to Elmer, giving him water. A pulley is a wheel with a rope that runs along the groove of the wheel.

This is called a fixed pulley. A fixed pulley is attached to a structure; therefore, it remains in a fixed position. A single fixed pulley changes the direction of the input force, but it does not magnify the input force.

Tools in Time

1100 A.D.   Europe

Crossbows were used in battle. Arrows shot from crossbows could pierce armor at 1200 feet.

Tools in Time

1250 B.C.   Greece

Homer made the story of the Trojan horse famous in his oral tales.

The fixed pulley does not magnify the force. It only changes the direction of the force. Max needs a new idea.

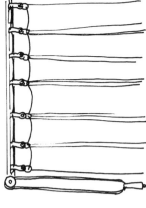

---

effort

load

Large construction cranes use moveable pulleys to lift heavy building materials to great heights.

Two things to remember when using a moveable pulley:

1) The load travels half the distance of the effort. For every foot you want the load to lift, you must pull the rope two feet.
2) The force needed to lift a load is half the weight of the load.

Elmer likes to drink the water from the pulley system that Max made. The only problem is that Max still has to get up to pull the rope for the pulley to work. That means that Max has to wake up when Elmer wants water. Plus, Elmer usually wants at least four glasses of water.

TECHNOLOGY

With the invention of heat engines, technology moved at an accelerated pace. Steam engines eventually became light and powerful enough to move locomotives across countries. The internal combustion engine was smaller and more efficient, and quickly replaced the steam engine. With the invention of the airplane came the need for a more powerful engine that would function well at high altitudes. In 1944, the jet engine was introduced.

Tools in Time

400 B.C.   **Italy**

A pulley system was used to lift loads of building materials.

Max builds another system. This time he attaches the wheel of the pulley to the load. Now the pulley moves up and down with the load. When Elmer pulls the rope the water comes to him because the direction of the force does not change. The load travels in the same direction as the force.

Another way the moveable pulley is different from the fixed pulley is that the force used to lift the load is magnified. Therefore, less force is required for Elmer to lift the load. The distance and speed are decreased, but less force is needed.

Max tries to think of a way that Elmer can apply the force to the pulley himself. With the pulley fixed to the bed, there does not seem to be any way for Elmer to do the work.

Tools in Time

1200 A.D.

Europe / India

A spinning wheel was used to make thread from wool.

Max needs a tool that does not change the direction of the force so that Elmer can do the work himself. This new tool also must magnify the force because Elmer needs a large amount of water each night.

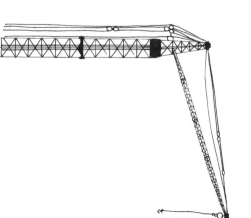

Another name for the compound pulley is a block and tackle.

load   effort

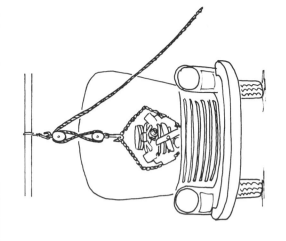

The compound pulley is used in elevators and lifts.

pulley
motor
pulley

pulley

With a compound pulley, the load travels half the distance of the effort. For every foot you want the load to lift, you must pull the rope two feet.

Elmer is sick. He is too sick to get out of bed. Max needs to take food up to him, but Max is afraid of heights.

Max decides to combine the two pulleys to get the most use out of both of them.

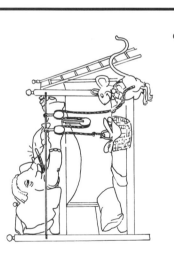

TECHNOLOGY

Life at home has become easier and healthier due to technology. Two factors contribute: Sewage systems allow cities to expand without the risk of disease; and electric power provides good lighting to homes and powers machines that make work easier. An early vacuum cleaner required two people to operate it: one to pump the bellows and one to steer the machine. Today electric power and the use of plastic parts makes the vacuum cleaner easy to use.

Tools in Time

500 B.C.   Greece
Artisans hammered bronze to make useful objects such as vases, mirrors, and kitchen utensils.

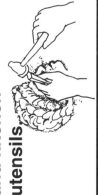
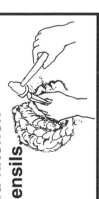

A compound pulley magnifies force, so it gives the worker a mechanical advantage.

A block and tackle is found in auto repair shops when heavy auto parts need to be lifted. This tool is also used to raise and lower scaffolding.

Max knows that the food is too heavy to move with a fixed pulley. Elmer is too sick to pull the moveable pulley. If only they had a system that magnifies force and changes the direction of the force.

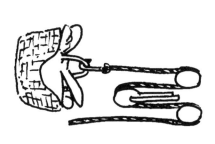

Max makes one fixed pulley and one moveable pulley. This combination magnifies force and allows the load to be moved upward by pulling down on the rope. This system is called a compound pulley.

Tools in Time

100 A.D.   Egypt

A compound pulley system was used for building large structures.

Tools in Time

1500 B.C.   Middle East

Hittite metal workers mastered iron making and guarded their secret for over 300 years.

The lever makes work easier by magnifying force. Levers are made of a rod and a fulcrum. There are three classes, or types, of levers. Look at these uses for levers.

A pulley consists of one or more wheels and a rope. There are three types of pulleys. All of them magnify force. Two of them change the direction of the force.

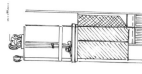

To open a can, you first squeeze the handles together. They are levers.

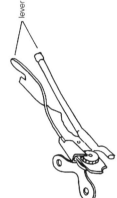

lever

A can opener uses three simple tools to work properly. Look closely to find the lever, wedge, and wheel and axle.

Remember that work is done when force is applied to a load and the load moves in the direction of the force. Tools make work easier. Let's review the six simple tools: inclined plane, wedge, screw, lever, wheel and axle, and pulley.

A wedge looks like an inclined plane, but it is used differently. The tip of the wedge moves into or under the load. When force is applied, the wedge pushes things apart. Here are some uses for the wedge.

TECHNOLOGY

Steam engines running on railroad tracks transported people and goods 50 years before the car. By 1850, with new materials in common use, steam powered road vehicles were possible. It was not until 1908 that Henry Ford made a car that the common man could afford to buy. He was not the first to use an assembly line, where each worker completes the same job on each car, but he made it work for a high volume of production.

Tools in Time

1230 B.C.   Egypt

To build pyramids, workers used many tools, such as ramps, wheels, and levers.

A wheel and axle makes work easier by magnifying force. When the wheel turns, the axle turns. When the axle turns, the wheel turns.

An inclined plane makes work easier by magnifying force. Here are some uses of the inclined plane.

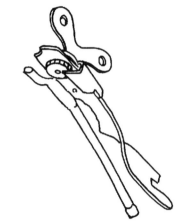
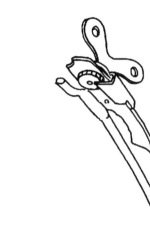

When two or more simple tools are used in one machine, it is called a complex machine. The wheel and axle on this plow makes the work easier to complete. This plow is a complex machine because it uses a wheel and axle and a wedge.

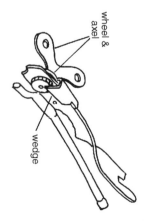

A screw is an inclined plane wrapped around a cylinder. The screw makes work easier because it offers more force. Friction helps the screw do its work. Here are some uses for the screw.

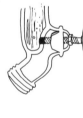

The part that pierces the can is a wedge. The handle that is turned to open the can is a wheel and axle.

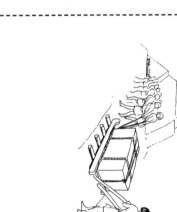

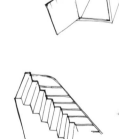

wheel & axle

wedge

drive gear

Sometimes the cogs of gears are linked together by a chain. The back gear of a bicycle is smaller than the front gear. This allows the rider's legs to move more slowly, since the smaller gear requires less force.

Bevel gears come together at an angle, changing force and direction.

All tools and machines are made of one or more of the six simple tools. Many machines use more than one simple tool. A machine that uses two or more simple tools is called a complex machine.

cog

TECHNOLOGY

Electronics and computing are 20th-century developments in technology. Microchips, which are essential elements of the science of electronics, were not invented until 1962. However, the rate of progress in the field of electronics has been extremely fast. Now, we can even use computers to help us design better computers! The computers of today can do thousands of times more than they could fifty years ago, and at much faster rates.

Tools in Time

300 B.C.   Egypt

Rack and pinion gears were used in water clocks.

The drive wheel can make a smaller wheel turn faster than it does, and it can make a larger wheel turn slower than it does. Count the cogs on the small gear. Count the cogs on the larger gear. The smaller gear must turn two times to make the larger gear turn once.

The big wheel rotates with twice the force and half the speed of the small wheel.

6

Spur gears lie next to each other, magnifying force, and reversing direction.

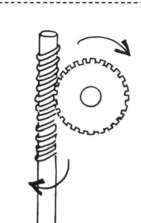

8

Worm gears have a wheel on a screw thread. Worm gears magnify and change the direction of the force.

11

Rack and pinion gears have one wheel and a rack with teeth. Instead of moving in a circle, rack and pinion gears move back and forth.

9

When the drive wheel gear turns, it causes the gear next to it to turn. The cogs interlock so that a cog on the drive wheel pushes on a cog of the next gear, making it turn.

4

Some tools are variations of simple tools. Gears are wheels with teeth along the outer edge. Most gears make work easier by magnifying force. The teeth of the gears are called cogs. Gears come in all sizes and vary in the number of cogs.

2

Tools in Time

725 A.D. China

Mechanical clocks were used with fairly good accuracy.

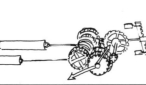

13

Tools in Time

80 B.C. Greece

Differential gears were developed in Greece.

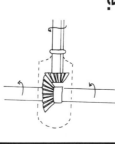

15

cam → / cam →

open

closed

crank

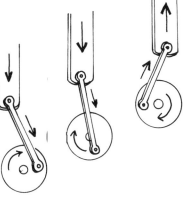

A sewing machine makes a stitch with two threads. One thread is in the eye of the needle, and the second thread is below the fabric. The needle moves down through the fabric, loops through the second thread, and comes up to form the stitch.

A sewing machine uses cams and cranks to do its work. A crank drives the needle up and down, and two trains of cams and cranks operate the feed-dogs that move the fabric.

Sometimes we need a tool to do a special job. When a simple tool will not do the job just right, a change has to be made to the tool.

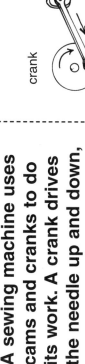

down →

← cam

up →

← cam

TECHNOLOGY

Disease and death have always been a part of life, and people through the ages have sought ways to heal the body. Today, technology helps doctors to find diseases through diagnostic imaging devices like ultrasound, MRI scans, and computerized EEG (brain) scans. Doctors can perform complicated surgeries with the use of a laser, and they can even transplant organs, like kidneys and hearts. Advances in technology are helping people to live longer and have a better quality of life.

Tools in Time

700 B.C.   Persia

Farmers used windmills to grind their grain.

A crank is also used in many machines. A crank is a wheel with a rod attached to it. The other end of the rod is hinged so that it moves backward and forward as the wheel turns.

feed-dogs

cranks

cams

cranks

cams

motor

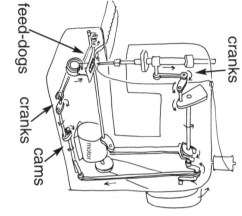

One of these special tools is a cam. A cam is a wheel and axle, but the wheel has an extension added to it. The extension usually pushes another part in a machine. As the cam turns, the part of the machine that the extension pushes against moves up and down.

Inside the cylinder of a car engine, a piston moves up and down. A connecting rod links the piston to a crank on the crankshaft. As the piston moves up and down, the crankshaft turns around.

crankshaft

A car's engine has cylinders that take in gas and release exhaust. This action is controlled by a valve. A cam operates the valve by forcing it down against a spring.

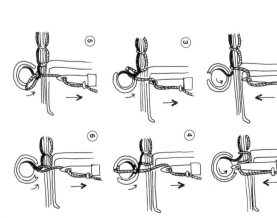

Tools in Time

1400 A.D.   Europe

Mechanical clocks were very accurate and were found in most households.

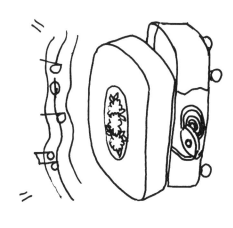

A torsion bar, or anti-roll bar, acts like a spring. If the bar is forced to twist in one direction, it resists and twists back when the force stops. Many cars have a torsion bar between the front axles to keep the car from rolling too far in one direction.

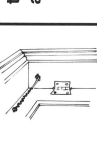

Springs make riding in a car smoother when you go down a bumpy road. Heavy springs between the wheel and axle and the body of the car absorb the bumps.

Shock absorbers help slow down the movement of the springs, making the drive less bumpy, too.

Springs play an important role in many machines that we use. Some of these machines are small, such as a stapler, and some are large, like a car.

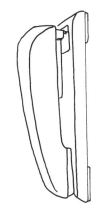

---

open door   closed door

extended spring

previous position of spring

TECHNOLOGY

Advances in technology, with the development of new machines, materials, and methods of working, have brought success and easier lifestyles to many people. Some, however, view trends in technology as threatening to our way of life. They are concerned because technology is dependent upon energy from fuels that cannot be replaced. Also, technology has introduced many disposable items into our world, creating a need to recycle. No matter how advanced we become technologically, there will always be problems to solve and frontiers to explore.

Tools in Time

600 A.D.   Rome

Windmills were used to make flour from grain.

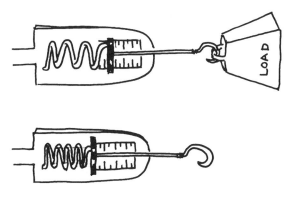

A stapler uses a spring to hold staples in place. This ensures that a staple will be in position when the stapler is pressed down. When one staple is used, the spring moves the next staple into position. The energy of the spring does the work.

The third use of the spring in machines is to store energy. When you compress a spring or stretch a spring, you use energy. This energy can be released immediately, as in a door spring, or gradually, as in a spring-driven music box.

spring

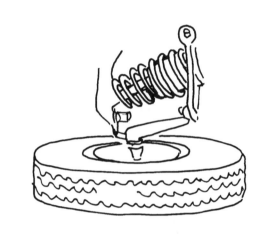

Springs have three main uses in machines. The first job is to return something to its previous position. A door spring will stretch when the door is opened. When the door is released, the spring will return to its previous position, closing the door.

The second use for a spring is in weighing machines. The spring begins in its original position. When a load is added to it, the spring stretches. The amount of stretching will determine the weight of the load.

Tools in Time

1902 A.D. Great Britain

Disc brakes were used. This brake squeezed both sides of a steel disc inside the wheel.

Let's focus on one tool that has not changed much over thousands of years, except in the way it is powered. Farmers have used the plow for as long as people have been growing crops.

Later, farmers hooked up their plows to animals. Plowing with animals took less effort for the farmer than pushing the plow himself.

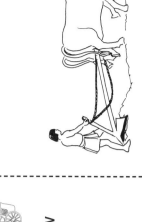

Simple tools are useful because they make our work easier to complete. Simple tools can be used by one person without help.

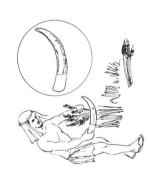

Lots of Science Library Book #24

steam engine plow

The power of wind and water made the use of very large tools possible.

TECHNOLOGY

In the early 1900s, many people of Papua New Guinea were still using stone spears and axes. These people lived in the jungles of the island, hunting, fishing, and farming for food. During World War II, some of these same people were introduced to the modern world when a helicopter landed near their homes. They went from living in the Stone Age to experiencing Modern Age in one helicopter landing.

Lots of Science Library Book #24

Tools in Time

1939 A.D.   USA/USSR
The first modern helicopter was designed with a single main rotor and a small tail rotor.

Lots of Science Library Book #24

Combining two simple tools improved the plow. The wheeled plow made the farmer's work easier and he did not have to feed a large animal in order to plow.

First, the farmer pushed the plow himself as he tilled his land.

Today, plows are still designed like the ones thousands of years ago. However, they are driven by powerful gasoline or diesel engines. Hydraulic systems enable farmers to control plows and other farming equipment from the driver's seat.

In 1832, the plow was powered by a steam engine. Now, farmers could use less effort to plow their fields, and they could plow larger areas of land.

The world of tools and technology changed dramatically when engines began to be used to power tools. Engines did not get tired, worked continuously, and could generate more power.

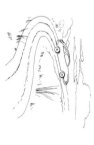

Large tools became easier to use when the power of an animal was used to make them work.

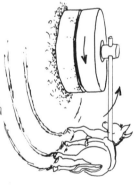

No machine can increase force and speed at the same time.

Tools in Time

1963 A.D.   Holland

The first cassette recorder was designed to use small cassettes instead of large reels of tape.

Tools in Time

1940 A.D.   Papua New Guinea

People used stone spears and axes to hunt and farm.

Graphics Pages

Note: The owner of this book has permission to photocopy the *Graphics Pages* for classroom use only.

Investigative Loop™

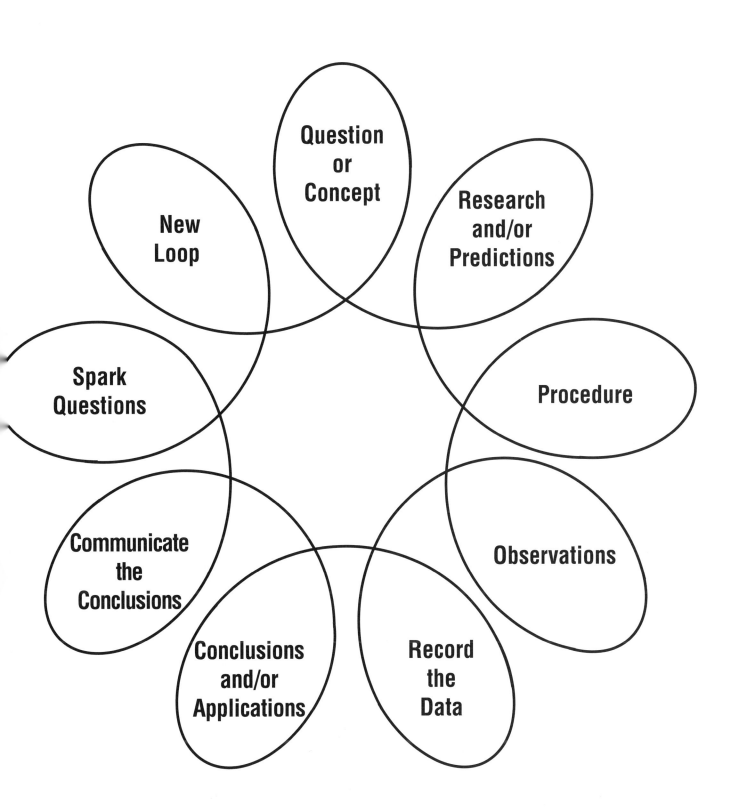

Question
or
Concept

Research
and/or
Predictions

New
Loop

Procedure

Spark
Questions

Observations

Communicate
the
Conclusions

Conclusions
and/or
Applications

Record
the
Data

Problem Solving and Inquiry Scenarios

Problem: Museum Exhibit Scenario

You are preparing an exhibit entitled "Tools Used to Build the Great Pyramid" for a museum. Research the Great Pyramid and the tools available to the Egyptians for its construction. Plan how you will present your findings. How can you make the exhibit interesting? How can you communicate interesting facts pertaining to the Great Pyramid and its engineering? Could you make examples of the tools used and explain their purpose?

Example Information: Over a twenty-year period, 2.5 million limestone blocks were used to build the Great Pyramid for Pharaoh Khnumu-Khufu.

The pyramid's limestone blocks weighed from two to over seventy tons each. Some of the blocks were difficult to cut because they contained large fossil shells.

Problem: Survival Scenario

You and your fellow students are castaways on an unpopulated island and you have to use native materials to make tools to help you survive and/or escape. You arrive on the island with only the clothes you are wearing and the personal items you are carrying. Empty your pockets and purses to see what you normally carry with you that would help you survive.

Establish the longitude and latitude of the imaginary island. Describe the climate of the island and its habitat, based upon its geographic location. Investigate other lands (islands or continental shores) within the geographic region. List and draw examples of possible flora and fauna. Determine the land features and topography of your imaginary island. Map the island. Describe prevailing winds and currents based upon information gained via National Oceanic and Atmospheric Administration (http://www.noaa.gov/). Develop a survival plan. Sketch tools that you have designed and explain their use. Don't forget to prioritize needs and wants. For example, what would be more important to have, food or fresh water? Work in small groups and keep personal journals describing daily progress.

Problem: Community Restoration Scenario

You have volunteered to help with a community restoration project. The house you have been assigned to is in need of painting, as well as roofing and carpentry repairs. Draw your house before, during, and after repairs. List the things that need to be done and list the tools you will need to accomplish the repairs. Describe the tools as simple or complex. Explain the use of each simple tool. Compare and contrast the work accomplished by simple machines and complex machines.

Alternative Activity: Develop a scenario based upon the Habitat for Humanity program.

Problem: Pitch a Television Show

Write the script for a television show based upon a character that can get out of any difficult situation by making tools out of unusual objects. Develop the character's appearance, speech, actions, and personality. Outline and write several segments for the television series. If possible, for inspiration, watch reruns of the 1980's MacGyver television show.

Problem: Build a Bird Nesting Box

Imagine that you are part of a local bird watch and rescue program, or become actively involved in a local birding project. Design and build a nesting box for a bird common to your area. Research the species of bird you select. Learn the size and shape of the bird's preferred nesting boxes. Discover how nesting boxes are mounted and at what height. Do you need to make provisions for cleaning the box? tagging the birds? observing eggs and young? Collect the tools and wood you will need to make a nesting box. With adult help and supervision, build a nesting box. Note the tools that you use to complete this project. How do these tools help you do work? Are some of the tools powered by something else?

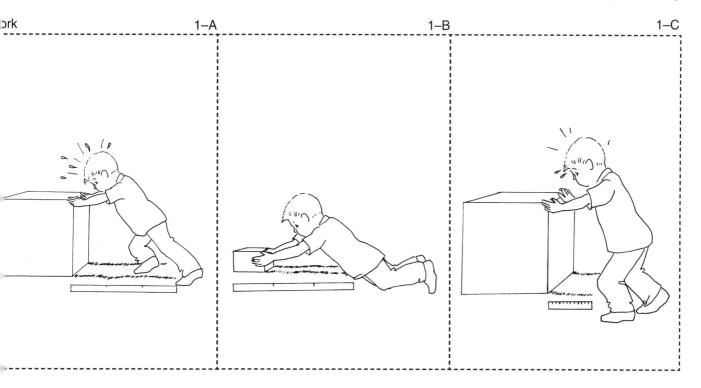

ork　　　　　　　　1–A　　　　　　　　1–B　　　　　　　　1–C

through 1–G　　　　　　　　Cut on the dotted lines

	4000 B.C.
9 B.C.	3000 B.C.
9 B.C.	2000 B.C.
9 B.C.	

1000 B.C.

99 B.C.

1 B.C.

.D.

1000 A.D.

01 A.D.

1300 A.D.

01 A.D.

1800 A.D.

01 A.D.

1900 A.D.

01 A.D.

2000 A.D.

Tools in Time   1–P   Jordan

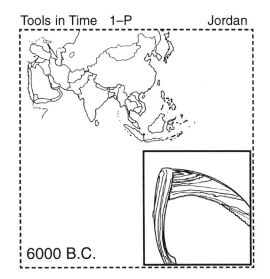

6000 B.C.

Tools in Time   1–Q   Yugoslavia

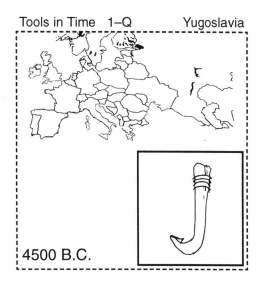

4500 B.C.

Friction 2–A 2–B 2–C 2–D

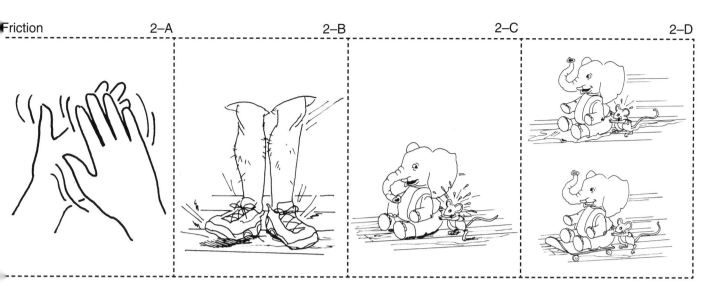

Tools in Time 2–E Europe

Tools in Time 2–F France

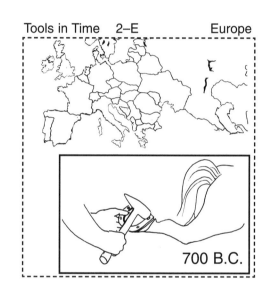

700 B.C.

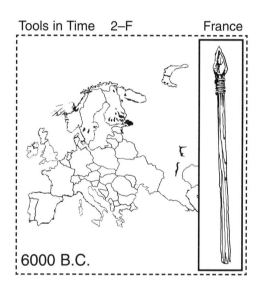

6000 B.C.

Experiencing Friction Lab 2–1 Reducing Friction Lab 2–2

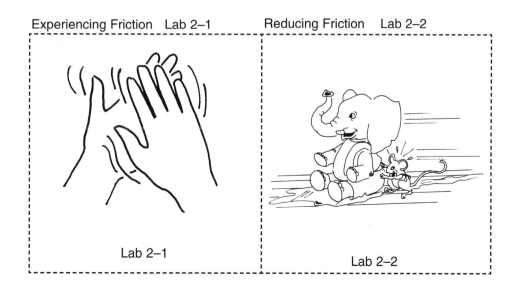

Lab 2–1 Lab 2–2

Types of Friction 3–A 3–B

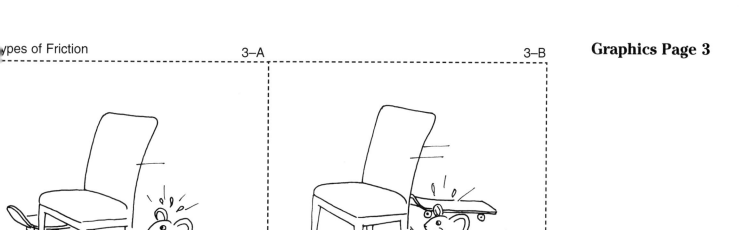

3–C

Tools in Time 3–D Northern Europe

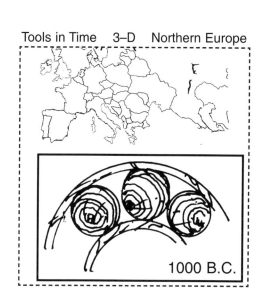

1000 B.C.

Compare Types of Friction Lab 3–1 The Race Lab 3–2

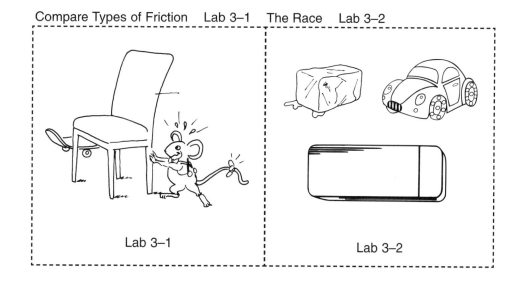

Lab 3–1 Lab 3–2

Tool Sign   4—A

Tools in Time   4—B   Roman Empire

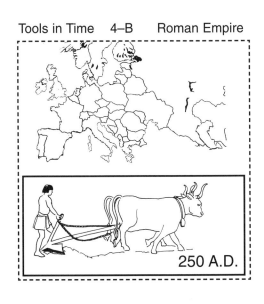

250 A.D.

How to Magnify Force   Lab 4—1

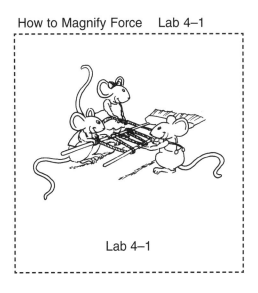

Lab 4—1

Inclined Plane   5–A

Inclined Plane   5–B

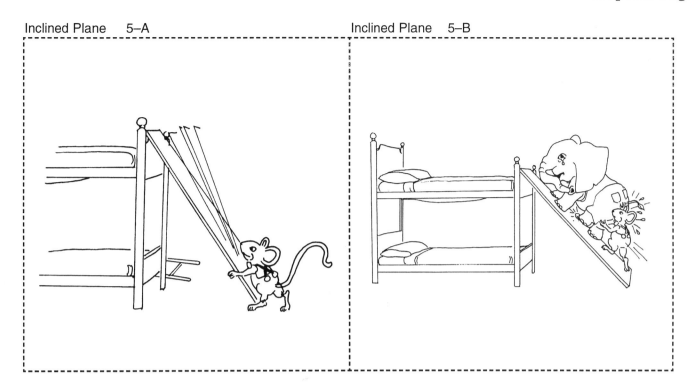

ɔls in Time   5–C   Jericho

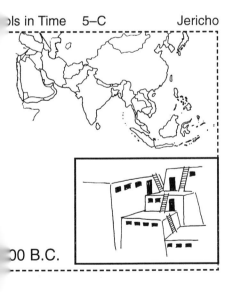

00 B.C.

ork and the Inclined Plane

6–B

6–C

6–D

6–E

Inclined Planes   6–A

Work and the Inclined Plane

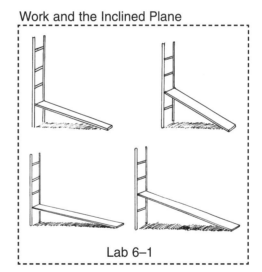

Lab 6–1

Tools in Time   6–F   Mesopotamia

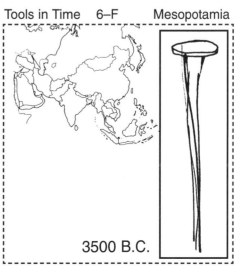

3500 B.C.

What is a wedge?   7–A

What is a wedge?   7–B

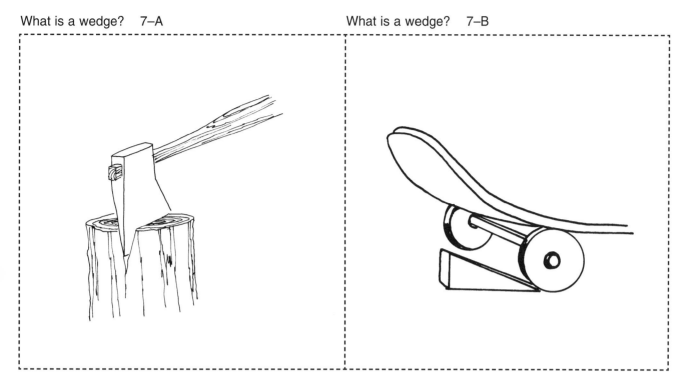

Tools in Time   7–E   China

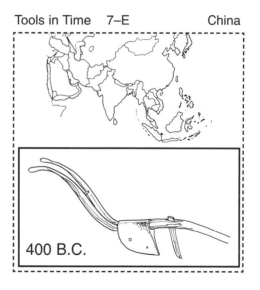

400 B.C.

es   7–C

"Make a Wedge" Directions

1. Cut out the wedge rectangle on the dotted line.
2. Glue the wedge rectangle onto thin cardboard or poster board.
3. Cut around the wedge pattern.
4. Fold down on the solid lines.
5. Put dots of glue on the section marked "glue".
6. Put the glued section under the opposite end of the rectangle to make a wedge.

7–D

glue

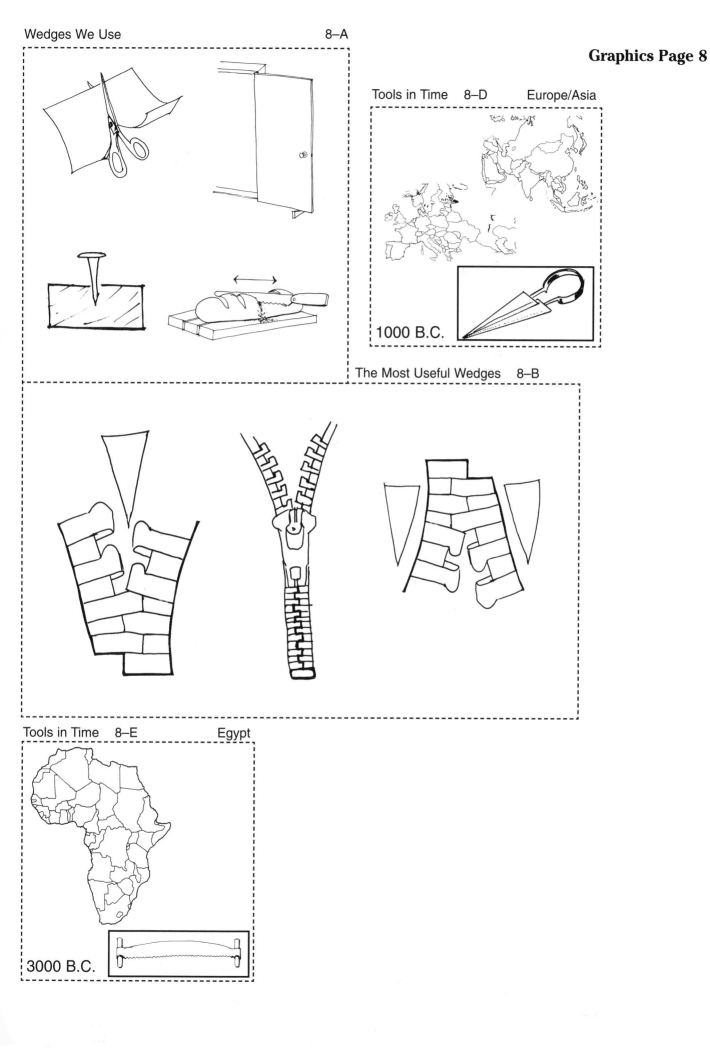

Wedges We Use   8–A

Graphics Page 8

Tools in Time   8–D   Europe/Asia

1000 B.C.

The Most Useful Wedges   8–B

Tools in Time   8–E   Egypt

3000 B.C.

8–C

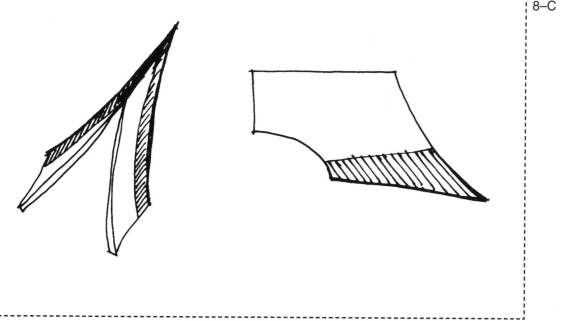

What is a Screw?   9–A

What is a Screw?   9–B

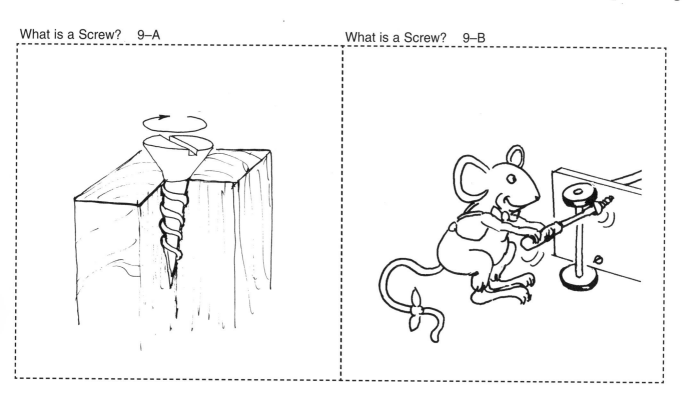

9–C

"Make a Screw" Directions

☐ 1. Cut out Section A and Section B.

☐ 2. Roll Section A like a Hot Dog, into a pencil–sized cylinder.

☐ 3. Glue the cylinder along the outer edge.

☐ 4. Cut on the lines that represent the pitch of the screw in Section B.

☐ 5. Glue the long end of Section B to the cylinder.

☐ 6. Wind Section B around the cylinder.

☐ 7. Glue Section B in place to make a screw.

Tools in Time   9–F   Europe

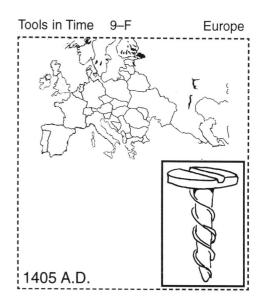

1405 A.D.

Tools in Time   9–G   Mesopotamia

1450 B.C.

ke a Screw   9–D

9–E

Section A cylinder

pitch lines ⟶

Section B inclined plane

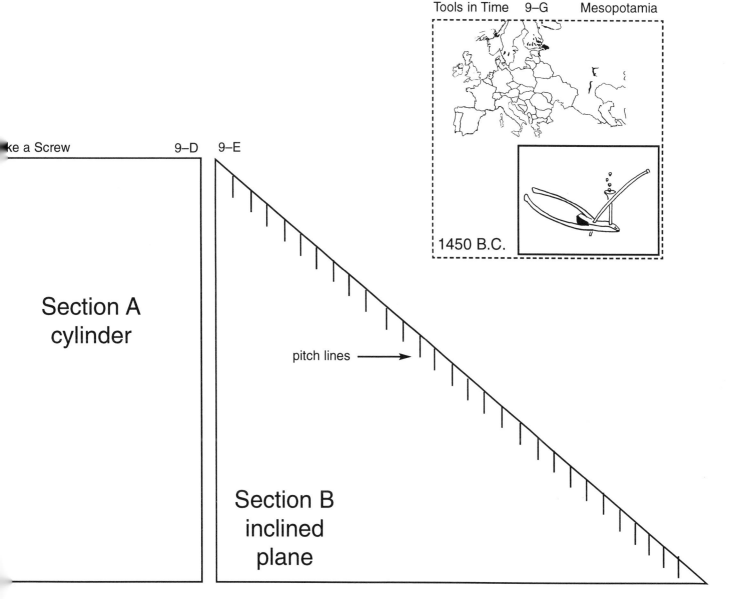

Screws We Use   10–A

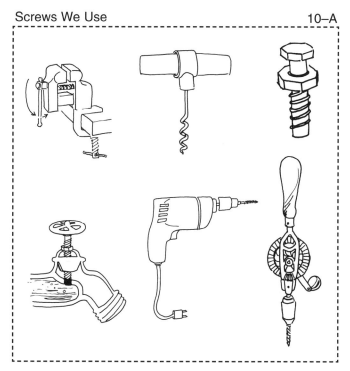

Tools in Time   10–B   Greece

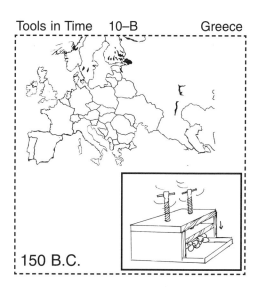

150 B.C.

Tools in Time   10–C   France

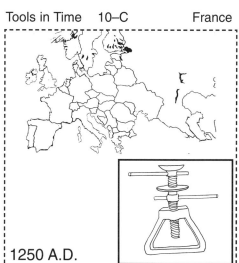

1250 A.D.

What is a Lever?   11–A

load   fulcrum   rod   effort

crum — 11–C

rod — 5 — 11–D

— 4 —

— 3 —

glue

11–E

— 2 —

— 1 —

What is a Lever?–Inside — 11–B

"Make a Lever" Directions

1. Cut out the fulcrum.
2. Glue it onto thin cardboard or poster board.
3. Cut it out and fold down on the solid lines.
4. Put glue on the "glue" section.
5. Put the glue section under the opposite end of the rectangle to make a fulcrum.
6. Cut out the rod.
7. Trace around the rod on five pieces of thin cardboard or poster board.
8. Cut out each piece and glue them together, one on top of the other.
9. Glue rod piece 11D, on top of the stack made in #8, being sure the numbers are on top.

Tools in Time — 11–F — Greece

1650 B.C.

ols in Time   11–G   Egypt

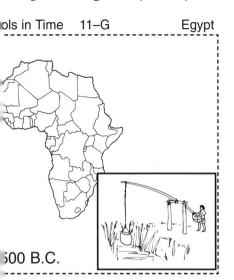

600 B.C.

Class One Levers   12–A

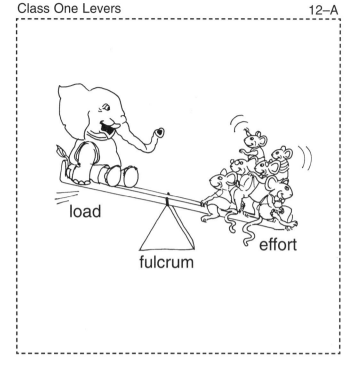

load

fulcrum

effort

Using a Class One Lever   Lab 12–1

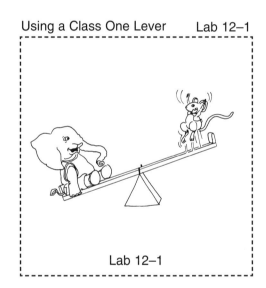

Lab 12–1

Class One Levers – Inside   12–B

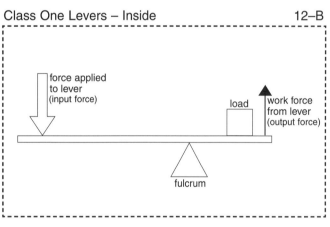

force applied
to lever
(input force)

load

work force
from lever
(output force)

fulcrum

Tools in Time   12–C   Egypt

2000 B.C.

Tools in Time   12–D   Egypt

2500 B.C.

Class Two Levers   13–A

Class Two Levers – Inside   13–B

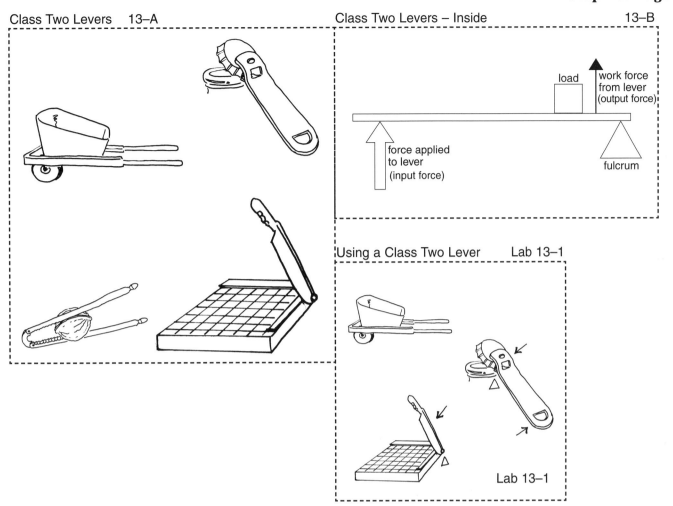

load

work force
from lever
(output force)

force applied
to lever
(input force)

fulcrum

Using a Class Two Lever   Lab 13–1

Lab 13–1

Tools in Time   13–C Northern Europe

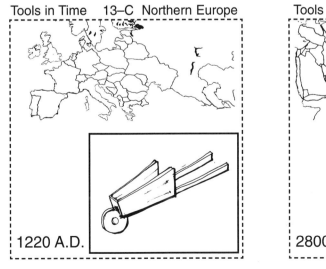

1220 A.D.

Tools in Time   13–D   China

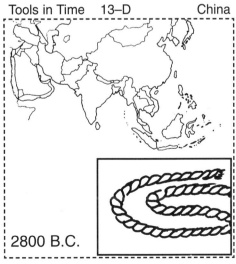

2800 B.C.

Class Three Levers   14–A

Class Three Levers – Inside   14–B

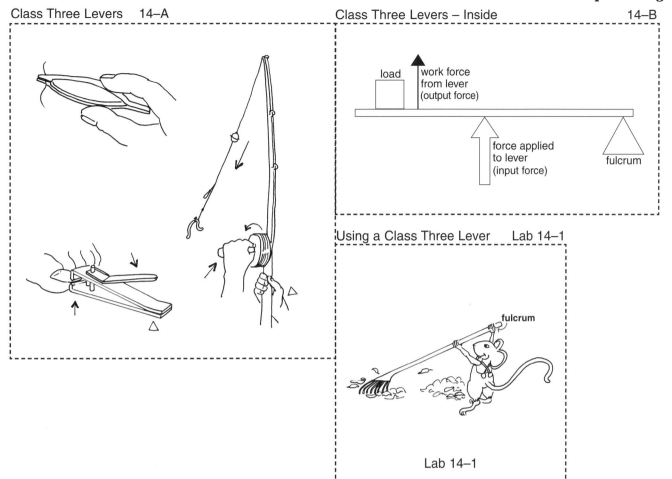

load

work force
from lever
(output force)

force applied
to lever
(input force)

fulcrum

Using a Class Three Lever   Lab 14–1

fulcrum

Lab 14–1

Tools in Time   14–C   China

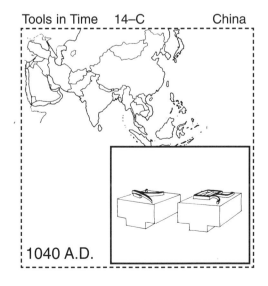

1040 A.D.

Tools in Time   14–D   Germany

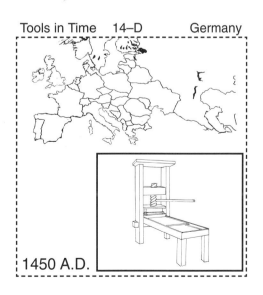

1450 A.D.

The Wheel and Axle   15–A

The Wheel and Axle   15–B

15–C

Make a Wheel and Axle" Directions

1. Cut out the wheel for a pattern.
2. Trace it on four pieces of thin cardboard or poster board.
3. Cut out the four wheels.
4. Punch a hole inside each wheel.
5. Glue two wheels together.
6. Glue the other two wheels together.
7. Use a pencil or straw as an axle.
8. Insert the axle in the holes of each wheel.
9. Secure in place with glue or tape, if needed.

15–D

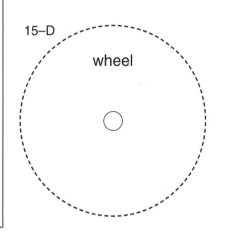

wheel

Experience the Wheel and Axle   Lab 15–1

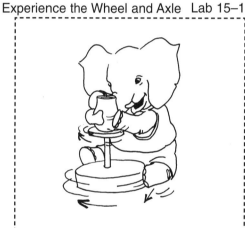

Lab 15–1

Tools in Time   15–C   India

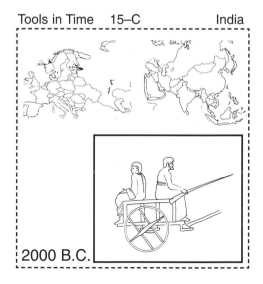

2000 B.C.

Tools in Time   15–D   Iraq

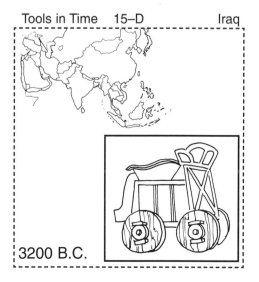

3200 B.C.

ols in Time   15–E   Greece

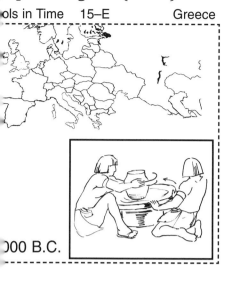

000 B.C.

ols in Time   16–B   Assyria

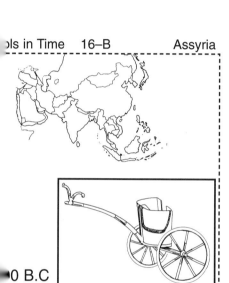

0 B.C

s in Time   16–C   Europe

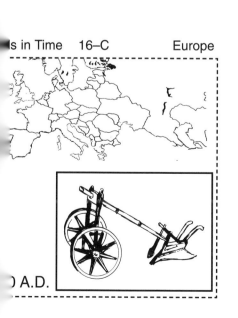

0 A.D.

The Wheel and Axle   16–A

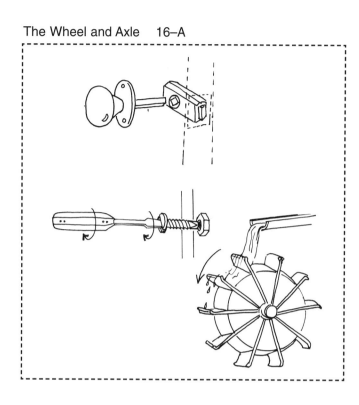

Graphics Page 17

The Fixed Pulley   17–A   17–B

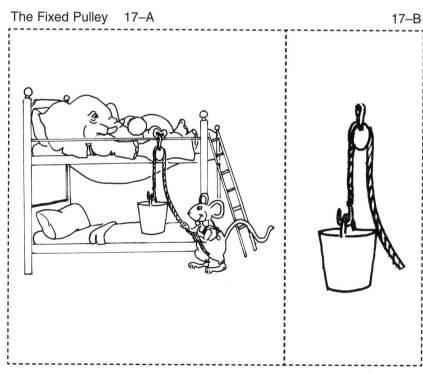

"Make a Pulley" Directions

❑ 1. Cut out the two wheels for patterns.
❑ 2. Trace 18 of the inside wheels on thin cardboard or posterboard.
❑ 3. Cut out the 18 circles and punch a hole in each one.
❑ 4. Glue 6 of the circles together, matching the holes.
❑ 5. Glue 6 more of the circles together, matching the holes.
❑ 6. Glue the last 6 circles together, matching the holes.
❑ 7. Put these 3 wheels aside.
❑ 8. Trace 6 of the outside wheels on thin cardboard or posterboard.
❑ 9. Cut out the 6 circles and punch a hole in each one.
❑ 10. Hold one of the smaller wheels and glue a large one on each side of it, matching the center holes.
❑ 11. Hold another one of the smaller wheels and glue a large one on each side of it, matching the center holes.
❑ 12. Hold the last of the smaller wheels and glue a large one on each side of it, matching the center holes.
❑ 13. Insert a 12" string through the center hole. Tie the string at the ends. Tack the top of the string to a board to make a fixed pulley

Experience the Fixed Pulley   Lab 17–1

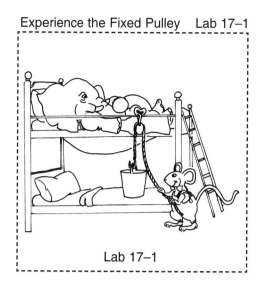

Lab 17–1

ols in Time 17–G   Rome

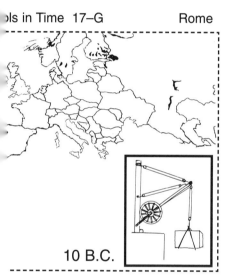

10 B.C.

Make a Pulley   17– D–E

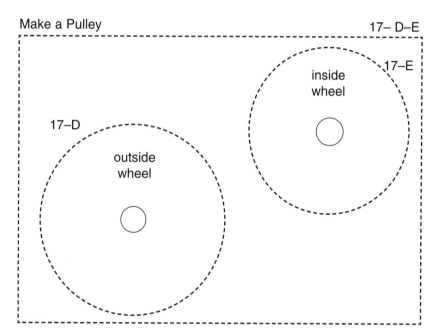

17–E

inside wheel

17–D

outside wheel

ls in Time 17–H   Greece

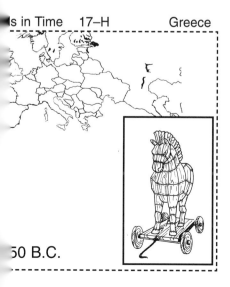

50 B.C.

Tools in Time 17–I   Europe

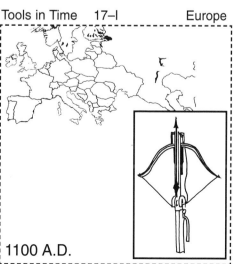

1100 A.D.

—F

Volume 15

Tools
Today and Tomorrow

The Effectiveness of Pulleys

Information on the use of different types of pulleys

The Moveable Pulley   18–A

18–B

Experience the
Moveable Pulley   Lab 18–1

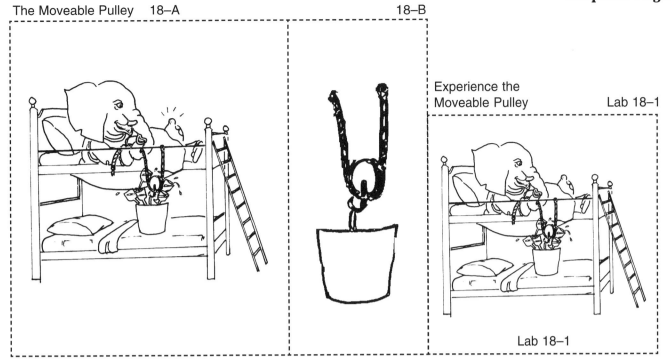

Lab 18–1

Tools in Time   18–C   Europe/India

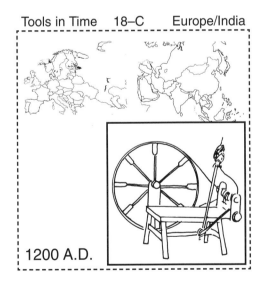

1200 A.D.

Tools in Time   18–D   Italy

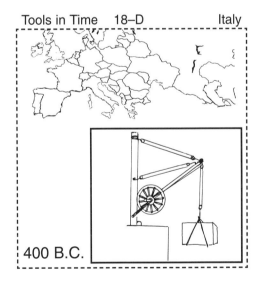

400 B.C.

e Compound Pulley   19–A

19–B

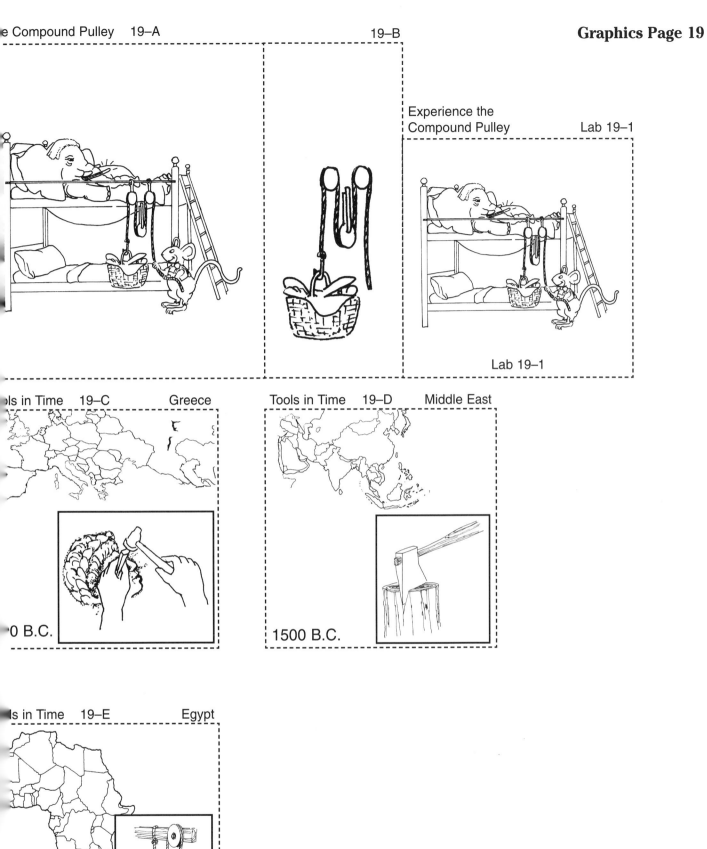

Experience the
Compound Pulley   Lab 19–1

Lab 19–1

ls in Time   19–C   Greece

0 B.C.

Tools in Time   19–D   Middle East

1500 B.C.

ls in Time   19–E   Egypt

0 A.D.

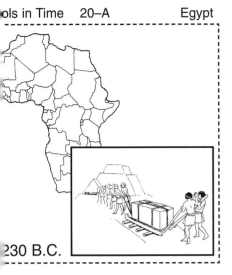

230 B.C.

es of Gears   21–A   21–B

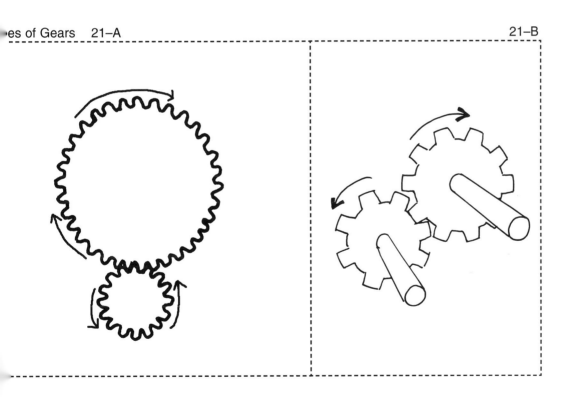

Types of Gears   21–C   21–D   21–E

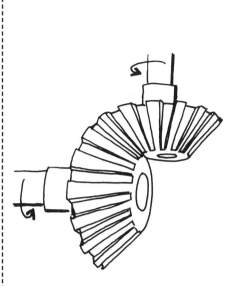

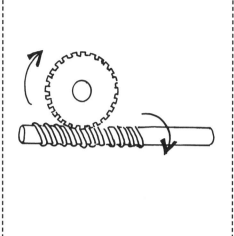

21–F

"Make Gears" Directions

❑ 1. Cut a piece of poster board 6"x1".
❑ 2. Form a circle with the strip, overlap it 1/2", and glue in place.
❑ 3. Cut a piece of poster board 10 1/2"x1".
❑ 4. Measure and mark every 1/2" on the 10 1/2" strip.
❑ 5. Fold the strip in this manner: fold the first 1/2" mark up; fold the next two 1/2" marks down; fold the next two 1/2" marks up. Continue until the whole strip is complete.
❑ 6. Glue the 10 1/2" folded strip onto the outside of the circle made in #2.
❑ 7. Cut a piece of posterboard 12"x1".
❑ 8. Form a circle with the strip, overlap it 1/2", and glue in place.
❑ 9. Cut a piece of poster board 20 1/2"x1".
❑ 10.Mark and fold the strip as in Steps 4 and 5.
❑ 11.Glue the 20 1/2"x1" folded strip onto the outside of the circle made in #8.

Tools in Time   21–G   China

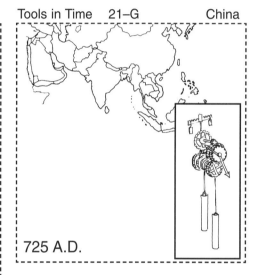

725 A.D.

Tools in Time   21–H   Egypt

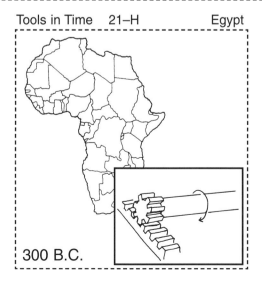

300 B.C.

Tools in Time   21–I   Greece

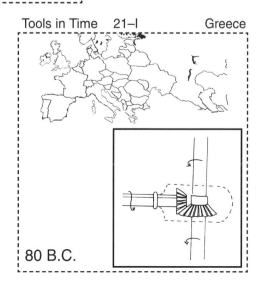

80 B.C.

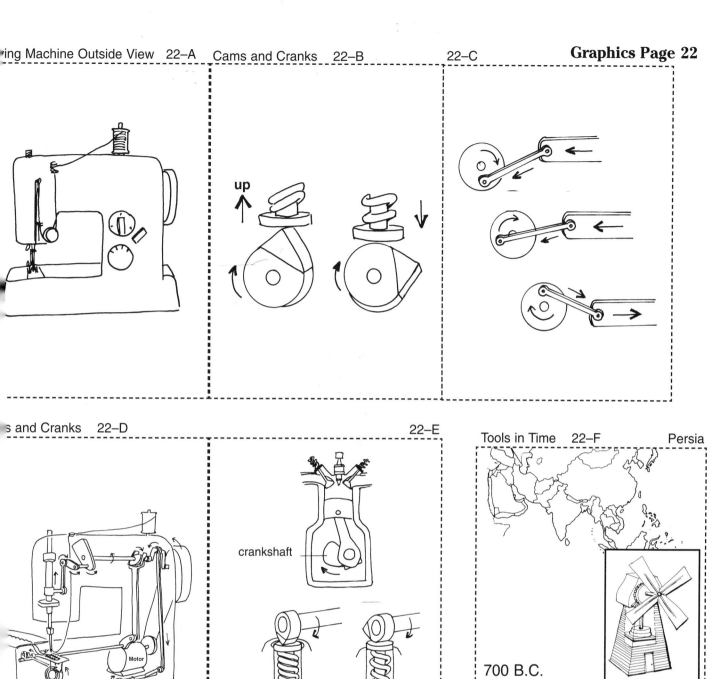

up

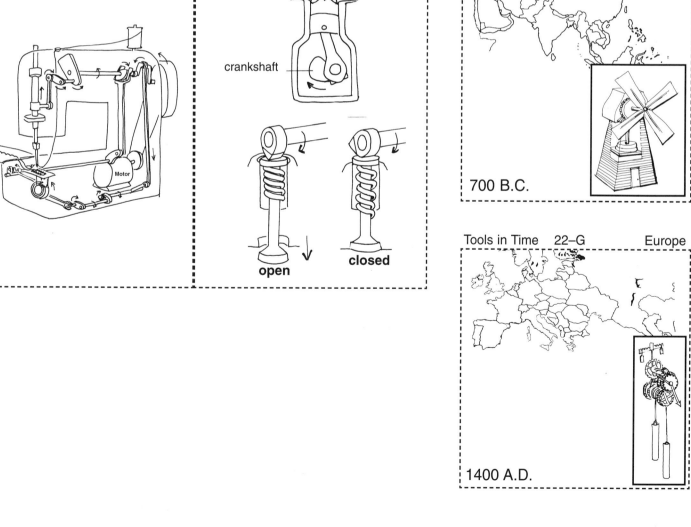

crankshaft

Motor

open   **closed**

Tools in Time   22–F   Persia

700 B.C.

Tools in Time   22–G   Europe

1400 A.D.

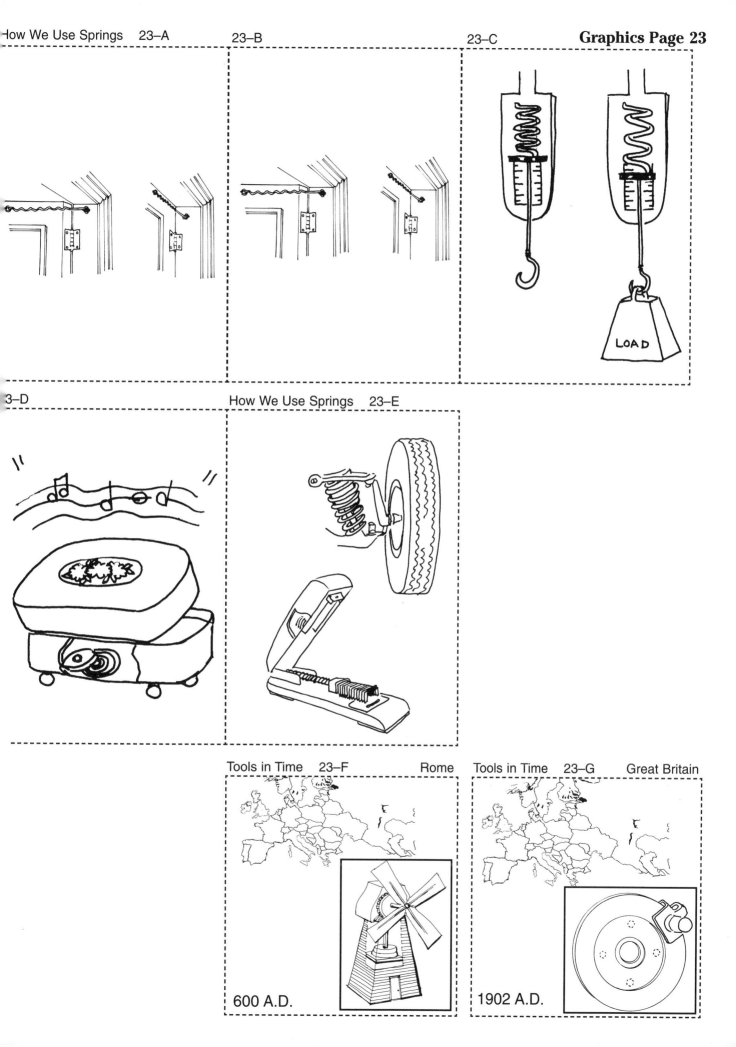

LOAD

3–D   How We Use Springs   23–E

Tools in Time   23–F   Rome

600 A.D.

Tools in Time   23–G   Great Britain

1902 A.D.

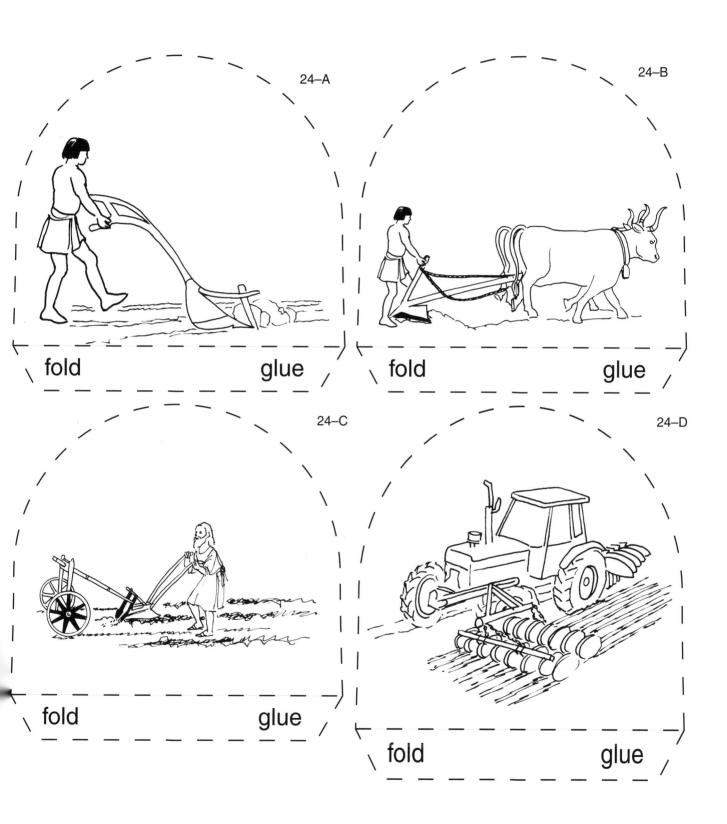

24–A

fold   glue

24–B

fold   glue

24–C

fold   glue

24–D

fold   glue

Tools in Time   24–E   Holland

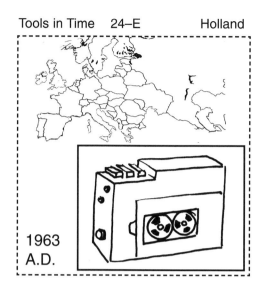

1963
A.D.

Tools in Time   24–F   USA/USSR

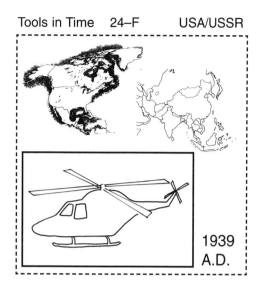

1939
A.D.

Tools in Time 24–G Papua New Guinea

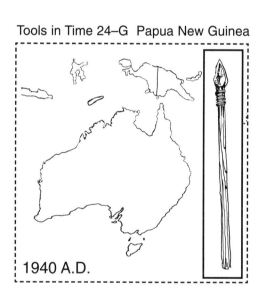

1940 A.D.

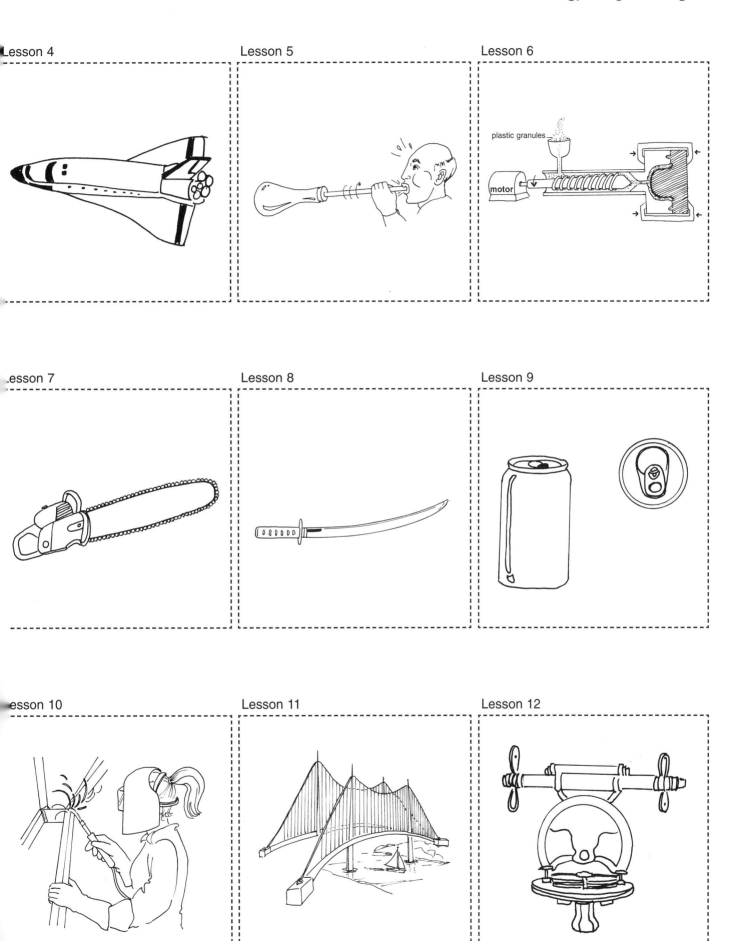

Lesson 4

Lesson 5

Lesson 6

plastic granules

motor

Lesson 7

Lesson 8

Lesson 9

Lesson 10

Lesson 11

Lesson 12

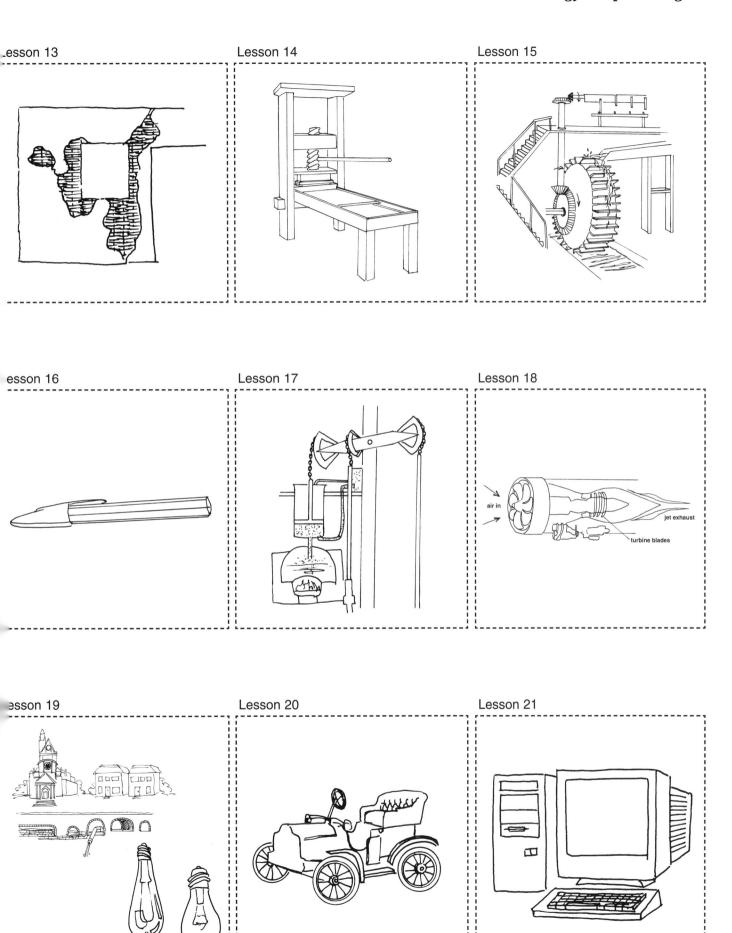

Lesson 13

Lesson 14

Lesson 15

Lesson 16

Lesson 17

Lesson 18

air in

jet exhaust

turbine blades

Lesson 19

Lesson 20

Lesson 21

Lesson 22

Lesson 23

Lesson 24

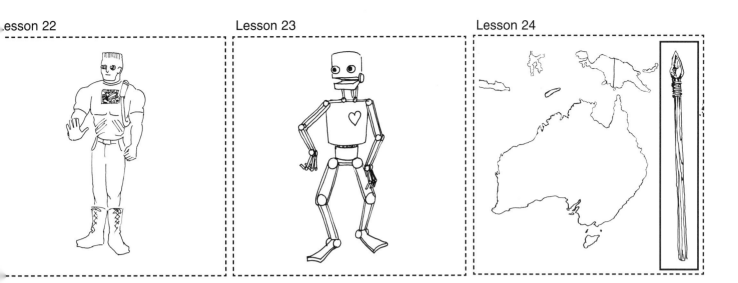